LIVING WITH MENTAL ILLNESS

LOUGHBOROUGH COLLEGE LIBRARY

AUTHOR	KUIPERS & BEBBINGTON
TITLE	Living with mental illness
CLASSMARK	

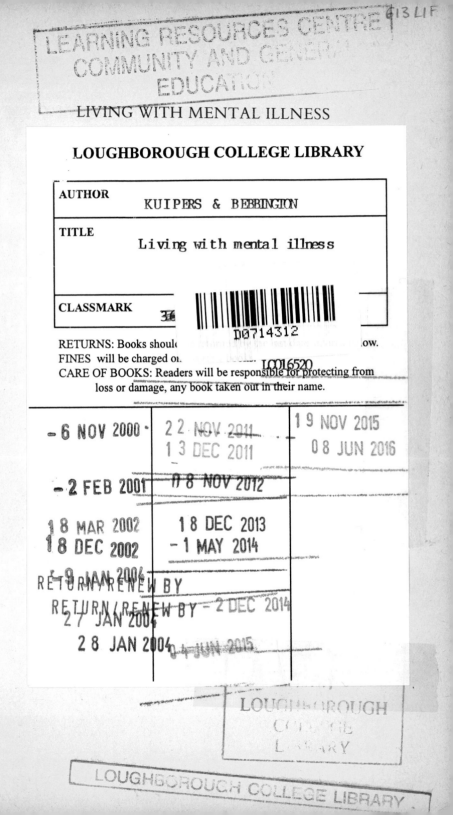

D0714312

LC016520

RETURNS: Books shoul ... ow.
FINES will be charged on ...
CARE OF BOOKS: Readers will be responsible for protecting from
loss or damage, any book taken out in their name.

HUMAN HORIZONS SERIES

LIVING WITH MENTAL ILLNESS

A Book for Relatives and Friends

LIZ KUIPERS, BSc, MSc, PhD
PAUL BEBBINGTON, MA, PhD, MRCP, MRCPsych

A CONDOR BOOK
SOUVENIR PRESS (E&A) LTD

ISBN 0 285 65052 1 casebound
ISBN 0 285 65053 X paperback

Printed and bound in Great Britain by
WBC Bristol and Maesteg

The Mental Health Foundation welcomes comments on the contents of this book. These will be filed and considered in any future edition, although we do not undertake to answer individual letters.

Foreword

This book was written in memory of two members of our family who suffered from mental illness. Our experiences with them made us appreciate the need for something specially written for those confronted by mental illness in someone close to them. We put the idea to the Mental Health Foundation, who approached Dr Kuipers and Dr Bebbington to write this book. We hope that the result of their enthusiasm and hard work may encourage relatives and friends.

Above all, we hope that it will help them to realise that they are not alone, and that many are facing similar experiences.

Reggie, Brian and Silvia Dingwall

Authors' Acknowledgements

The writing of this book has been greatly helped by the constructive criticisms of Rod Harper, Dick Thompson, John Wing and the Dingwall family. Our thanks are also due to the many relatives of psychiatric patients who have given us the necessary knowledge and incentive. Some have also commented on the book directly.

★　★　★

The cover illustration was painted by Annie Rae, a professional designer and illustrator who herself experienced a psychiatric illness from which she has now recovered.

Contents

Introduction

This book is intended for you, the relative or friend of a person affected by mental illness. Everybody knows of someone who has had a 'nervous breakdown', and for large numbers of us this means someone in the family. Even so, mental illness is more widespread than is generally realised. Not everyone is affected in the same way or to the same extent. In this book we have concentrated on the problems you may face if your relative suffers from the disorders called **schizophrenia** and **manic depressive illness**. These are among the most severe mental conditions, but even so are much more common than most people think. It is estimated, for instance, that more than 200,000 people in this country suffer from either chronic or relapsing schizophrenia. This is like the population of a small city, Derby for example. To put it another way: two people every day suffer a first attack of schizophrenia. Manic depressive illness is even more common. Where we work in south London, it is reckoned that about 15 per cent of the local people will be treated by a psychiatrist for depression at some time in their lives, although most of them will suffer relatively mild forms of the disorder. Psychiatrists do, of course, deal with other disorders, but these are mostly less taxing or, like dementia, begin towards the end of life.

Living with another person always takes a certain amount of skill and there are often tensions that arise from time to time. Not everyone is equally good at this, but a majority manage to keep their relationships going reasonably satisfactorily. We learn to do this from a young age, by watching others and by having our own sometimes temporary friendships. If you live with someone who develops schizophrenia or manic depressive illness, you are almost certain to be presented with problems that you have never met before, and that you may never even have heard about from anyone else. Some people in this situation are lucky and hit on good ways to cope with it from early on; others do not cope so well, and this may lead to further and increasing difficulties. They then often blame themselves for the way things have turned out. While this is understandable, it is not appropriate. If there were the equivalent of school courses in how to live with someone suffering from a severe mental illness, it would perhaps be a different matter, but there are not. In fact there is very little guidance at all, so people try to adapt their previous experiences to deal with the new situation. Unfortunately, this new situation is so different from anything they have previously known that old and tried methods of coping may not work. It is because schizophrenia and manic depressive illness can lead to difficulties of a rather particular and persistent kind, both for the sufferer and for relatives, that we have written this book especially for them.

Over the last twenty-five years in this country, there has been a strong movement towards a new policy in caring for the mentally ill. This has been called **community care**, and the main idea behind it was that patients should no longer be kept for long periods in old and poorly maintained mental hospitals. Instead, facilities were to be developed in the community — day hospitals, psychiatric wards in local general hospitals, day centres, group homes, hostels and the like. We have really seen precious few of the new facilities, but the policy of keeping people in hospital for much shorter periods has been followed energetically. The result, as you are likely to know, is that the burden of caring for the mentally ill has fallen increasingly upon their relatives.

A lot of psychiatrists and other health professionals are very concerned about the bad effects that the poor state of community care has had on the lives of patients and their relatives. This concern is also seen in the report of the House of Commons Select Committee on Social Services, published in 1985. It is a damning document that records the wholly inadequate funding and organisation devoted to carrying through the policy of community care. We personally still think that the policy is a good one in itself, but there is no doubt that it has been botched, and little sign that things will change much in the near future. This means that we have to live with it — sufferers, relatives and professionals all. In this far from ideal situation, we hope you will gain some support and help from this book.

If you live with someone who has schizophrenia or manic depressive illness you must have many questions you would like answered. We tried to think what these might be, and to answer them. The first chapter is mainly concerned with basic information about severe mental illness. We hope you will not find this too dry, but it has to cover a lot of ground. The next deals with problems you may have to face in living with your relative. Following this, two chapters are devoted to the various types of services and treatments. The fifth chapter covers the legal processes surrounding compulsory admission and treatment, and the safeguards that are built into the **1983 Mental Health Act**. This section is important, but will only be relevant to a few of you reading this book. The last chapter considers the feelings you might have about your situation and how you might cope with them. At the end of the book is an **Appendix of useful addresses** and an **index**.

We hope that a quick glance will tell you whether the book will help you. You are bound to have questions we have not covered, so do not be afraid to ask the people treating and caring for your relative for answers and advice. It is essential to realise that you can play an important part in the patient's progress to recovery. Although you may sometimes find things discouraging, helping your relative can also be very rewarding, and may be vital for him or her.

Mental illness is a field in which there are more uncertainties than facts. You may well come across professionals with very different views on particular subjects, and some will put them forward with total conviction! If you are not aware that mental health is an area where many questions are still waiting for an answer, this can be especially confusing. Sadly, many professionals are ignorant about the difficulties you are likely to experience in living with the patient. In fact, you are an expert in this field, at least in the sense that you have first-hand experience, and perhaps have already tried many of the suggestions made to you.

We have tried to avoid giving the appearance of being certain when we are not. After all, each situation is different. However, the suggestions we make have been found useful by other people in similar circumstances, and may work for you.

Finally, in the book we give examples from the situations and experiences of patients and relatives we have known. We think personal anecdotes add colour to what we have to say, and you may be able to identify with some of the stories. However, in the interests of confidentiality, we have disguised the identities of the people concerned.

1 Mental Illness

Mental illness is a loose term. It covers problems that some people have in connection with the way they **think**, **feel** or **behave**. Medically speaking, it covers **several different conditions**, and their effects can vary from the relatively trivial to the incapacitating.

It is sometimes difficult to distinguish mild states of, for instance, anxiety or depression, from ordinary moods, and indeed, the transition from what we think of as normal to the definitely abnormal is a gradual one. It is made more complicated because 'abnormal' can mean two different things: what is abnormal for a given person, and what would be abnormal for anyone. In general, we tend to recognise mental states as abnormal when, as a result, the sufferer is clearly and persistently unable to function properly in society. This is important because once we recognise that someone is psychiatrically abnormal, we are quite rightly prepared to make allowances, at least to some extent, in a way we would not if we thought he or she was merely misbehaving, or fooling about, or just being rather self-indulgent. This can be an issue even in the more severe psychiatric conditions that are the subject of this book.

For most of us mental illness is a disturbing and frightening thing. This is partly because people who are mentally ill behave in **unpredictable**, **unfamiliar and sometimes embarrassing** ways. It is particularly distressing when these changes happen to someone who is close to us. Worst of all, the mentally ill make us feel **helpless** — the normal ways of helping people do not seem to work. It is hurtful and confusing when we try to be sympathetic and supportive, and offer constructive advice, to find it rejected or misinterpreted, or just plain ignored.

It is frequently said that mental illness is an illness like any other. This is not quite true, however: after all, we respond to illnesses of the mind in a rather special way. When someone is physically ill, there is no problem about understanding his or her behaviour, because we see the reason for it: we ourselves might behave the same way in similar circumstances. However, it may not be possible to discover the reasons why mentally ill people behave as they do. Sometimes, the reasons are based on beliefs that are obviously untrue or appear incredible. Sufferers may also claim to have experiences which seem to be quite fantastic. This is upsetting, and it is not surprising that people shy away from the topic. They often use euphemisms like **suffering from nerves** or **nervous breakdown** to describe mental conditions.

For these reasons, mental illness is still associated with many **myths** and **misunderstandings**. Those who have been mentally ill often feel, with some justification, that they are shunned and stigmatised by society, though this is beginning to change. More open attitudes and more information will reduce some of the prejudices.

Psychiatrists cannot yet rely on any simple investigation, like a blood test, for finding out if someone has a particular mental illness, although there is considerable evidence that the more severe forms may be caused by subtle changes in **brain chemistry**. This being so, they can only recognise particular mental illnesses from the way people behave and the things they say. This business of recognising which illness someone has is called 'diagnosis'. Doctors always feel it is very important because, in theory at any rate, it narrows down the possibilities — the course the illness will take, the proper treatment to give, the likely response to it, and so on. Psychiatrists are also quite properly keen on diagnosis,

even though it is particularly difficult in their chosen field.
It is also less effective in its job of narrowing possibilities
than in more precise branches of medicine. This makes
psychiatry one of the most difficult specialties, with many
uncertainties. In consequence, it is easy for misunderstandings to arise between patients and their relatives and the
psychiatric team.

Experiencing a severe mental illness
Schizophrenia is one of the most severe mental illnesses. For
a medical condition, it is unusual in that it is seen all over
the world with a very similar frequency, in both modern
and traditional societies. It cannot therefore be said that it is
one of the burdens of modern civilisation. It occurs equally
in males and females although it starts a little later in women,
and has a slightly worse outlook in men. It is more common
among people lower down the social scale, but this is almost
certainly because sufferers do less well in life than they might
otherwise have done.

Oddly, it might be best to start by saying what schizophrenia is **not**. It is **not**, despite what many people believe,
a **split personality** of the Jekyll and Hyde type. There is
no rapid switch from perfect normality to a totally different,
often unpleasant, pattern of behaviour, so different that it is
as if the person has become someone else. Psychiatrists call
this rather rare condition 'hysterical split personality', not
schizophrenia.

The human mind has been described, fairly aptly, as being
like an orchestra. The separate functions of the mind —
thought, sensation, memory, emotions, and so on — can be
thought of as the instruments that make up this orchestra.
Normally these functions are integrated — that is, they play
together in harmony. What seems to happen in schizophrenia
is that this integration is somehow disrupted or 'split'. It is
as if the various instruments are all playing different tunes.
The result in an orchestra would be an indescribable and
painful jangling, the result for the mind is schizophrenia.

And so it is not the personality that is split, but the smooth dovetailing of the different functions of the mind. It is hard for those of us not affected to gain an insight into this terrible condition, but it results in sufferers being unable to trust their sensations and experiences and, by extension, the behaviour of those around them.

The doctor recognises schizophrenia mainly by the presence of **delusions**, **hallucinations** and **other unusual experiences**. Delusions are irrational beliefs, 'mad ideas', while hallucinations often take the form of imaginary voices. We describe these symptoms in more detail below on pp. 39–42.

The disease may start suddenly and dramatically, but it often follows a gradual deterioration: sufferers may become **less sociable** and **less able to study or work** in a consistent way. They may become **less affectionate** so that relatives find it hard to get through to them any more. In cases like this, with a gradual onset, the definite features of schizophrenia may appear only after months or even years. This makes it difficult for the psychiatrist to be sure what is happening, at least at the beginning.

Mary was an 18-year-old who developed a schizophrenic illness. She still lived at home, and had always been a shy person. She was very close to her widowed father. She enjoyed quiet activities like fishing, but would also go out to a pub or visit friends to play records. Over a period of some months, she felt less like going out. It made her feel very self-conscious, even a bit jittery. She did not really like the sense of being the centre of attention. However, she enjoyed the company of her friends, so she often invited them round. They were a bit boisterous, and Mary was glad just to sit on the sidelines watching them. It made her feel safe. However, because they were noisy, the neighbours complained one night and her father discouraged her from asking them round again, so she did not. She began to find that her usual chores were a real effort and, eventually, beyond her. Her elder brother came round one evening and dragged her out to a local pub. Mary did not want to go, and felt dreadful when she got there. She felt as if everyone was looking at her, that somehow they knew all about her and were talking about her. She made an excuse to leave as early as possible, but was still upset when she got home. The next evening something happened that made her feel even more frightened. While she was in her bedroom, she could hear people talking about her. There seemed no doubt about it, although when she looked out of the window and the door there was no one around. Moreover, the voices, whoever they were, were not being very nice about her, using language and making suggestions that upset her. She kept very quiet about this for a couple of days. However, she began to have strange fancies that seemed to grip her imagination, for instance, that she was pregnant. She thought she could feel the baby stirring inside her. As she had never made love with anyone, she could only have been made pregnant by a spirit or a ghost, and the more she thought about this the more convinced she became.

Finally Mary told her father what had been going on, and he called the family doctor immediately.

This story gives some idea of what it was like for one person who developed a schizophrenic illness. The experience differs in detail from case to case, but it is rarely anything but very unpleasant. The experiences Mary had, and some that she did not, will be described further when we write about the symptoms of the disease below. Remember, however, that what is a symptom to the doctor or relative is a very real experience to the sufferer.

Fortunately, Mary responded well to treatment and made a complete recovery, although she remained a rather shy and immature young woman. Clearly, it would have been very difficult for anyone to be sure what was going on in the early stages of this illness, or that it was anything more than 'just a phase'. Once the full picture emerged, however, there could be no doubt that Mary had schizophrenia.

There are, in fact, two sorts of symptoms in schizophrenia.

Hallucinations and delusions may be rather dramatic but are not usually present all the time. It is however, the **negative symptoms**, described on p. 44, which are really damaging. If the patient does not have any negative symptoms, he or she may be fairly well between attacks of the more dramatic symptoms. Indeed, some lucky patients may only have a single attack.

Simon was like this. He was a 33-year-old married man who worked as an electrical engineer. He seems to have been a cheerful and effective member of society before his illness. Following what appeared to be a minor problem at work, he suddenly became very frightened, and claimed that the local radio mast was controlling his brain. He was admitted to hospital where he was observed for a few days without being given any medication. His state of mind rapidly improved and after a few weeks he was able to take up his ordinary life again. So far he has not had any return of his mental symptoms.

What we call schizophrenia may be a number of different diseases, so it is hardly surprising that doctors sometimes find it difficult to give exact guidance about outlook, the need for particular treatments and so on.

The disease most commonly begins in early adulthood: two thirds of sufferers will have had their first attack by the time they are thirty. However, it can develop at any time of life, right up into old age. Maude was a 71-year-old woman who had followed a career in the civil service with some success. She was widowed, and her children lived in the next town. Some time before, she had had a minor difference of opinion with her next-door neighbour, and she became rather embarrassed whenever she met him, as the problem had never really been resolved. This became worse, so that she would avoid his eye rather than say good morning. Not surprisingly, the neighbour was not sure how to respond to this snub, and was rather embarrassed himself. Maude took this as indicating that he was ashamed of something, although she was not sure what it was. However, this gradually became clear to her: his shifty behaviour must be the result of something he was up to, and Maude reckoned that other little pieces of evidence confirmed that he was secretly making bombs for a terrorist group. This explained the rather unusual chemical smell she thought she could detect lingering about her own house and garden. Her children were never able to pick up this smell, and they were surprised at her allegations about the neighbour whom they had always previously found rather pleasant. Nor were they convinced by her claim that his wife had been passing messages to fellow conspirators by the order in which she hung clothes on the garden line.

Schizophrenia is very rare indeed before adolescence. It seems to require that the brain has matured to a certain point before it will emerge. Sometimes it comes out of the blue. Some sufferers, on the other hand, have always had eccentric, quirky or withdrawn personalities, but it must be said that most people like that do not develop schizophrenia.

Manic depressive illness is the other great mental affliction of adult life. About twice as many women as men suffer from it, and it, too, is widespread throughout the world. Many authorities think it may be on the increase, but the most severe types are probably becoming less common. Once more, it is probably not one but several conditions, and this is reflected in the many overlapping names that psychiatrists use to cover them. However, they are grouped together because their central feature is a disorder of **mood**. Mood is a word for feelings like happiness, sadness, fear or anger.

The word depression is often used in a casual way to describe anything from normal unhappiness to those abnormal moods that seem to be the result of an illness, and it is true that it may sometimes be hard to draw the line. The mood disturbance in manic depressive illness centres on happiness or sadness. However, it is far greater and more persistent than most of us normally experience. People are either hopelessly gloomy and miserable, looking at things in a very pessimistic light (**depression**) or wildly elated and energetic with big ideas about themselves and their abilities (**mania**). Another word for mood is **affect**, so manic depressive illness is sometimes called **affective illness**. One big division is between those patients who get both depressed and manic, and those who only get depressed. The first group are called **bipolar** because they move between the two **poles** of depression and elation. The second group are called **unipolar**, so you may hear clinicians referring to unipolar or bipolar affective illness. The bipolar type often begins in early adult life, whereas unipolar illness is more likely to emerge as people get older. Bipolar illness is actually quite rare, so most sufferers oscillate between normal mood and depression.

Another distinction you may hear about is that between depressive neurosis (or neurotic depression) and depressive psychosis (or psychotic depression). Psychosis and neurosis are terms that have lost their original meaning and have failed to acquire any very precise new meaning. Perhaps exactly because they are so sloppy, they have remained rather popular with psychiatrists. In general, a depressive psychosis is a severe depression, often with odd symptoms, sometimes with very odd ones like hallucinations and delusions (see pp. 39–41). A depressive neurosis looks more like an extreme form of normal misery, perhaps being maintained because the sufferer has a rather vulnerable personality. However, the two categories run into one another without much evidence of a clear boundary — there are many people whose condition falls midway between these two types.

However much clinicians may argue the finer points (and they do), a depressive illness makes a harrowing experience. Susan was a 24-year-old teacher who had married about three years previously. She and her husband had moved to London where they had bought a pleasant modern flat. She worked in a local infant school. She liked the work, although she did have opinions about teaching that had led to minor disagreements with the headmistress. Working as an infant teacher is always strenuous, but Susan usually had energy to spare.

However, over a period of a few weeks, she felt as though the work was becoming too much for her. She felt really tired when she got home, and unable to devote herself to the preparations she usually made for the next day's teaching. She normally cooked the evening meal, something she did efficiently and almost automatically, but this, too, she found had become a real effort. Somehow she got through her days but then lay around in the evening in an exhausted state. In the past, she and her husband had enjoyed going out together, but now she felt this to be completely beyond her: she made excuses and her husband fell in with this quieter life fairly amicably, feeling merely that she was going through a tough patch at school and would benefit from the rest. He was solicitous and tried to support and comfort her. One evening, although he had a suspicion that this might be difficult, he moved from gentle affection into love-making. This distressed Susan greatly although she tried, not very successfully, to hide it. Not being able to respond sexually was bad enough, but she also felt completely out of touch with her normal affection for him, almost as if he was a stranger. She began to feel that a woman like that could not be much good, and her sense of guilt became laceratingly painful. She became unable to think of anything except her agonising preoccupation with herself and her feelings. She could hardly do anything, and she felt slow, stupid and old. Her husband, meanwhile, was becoming increasingly and desperately worried about her. She still drove herself to go to work, but one morning the burden became too much and she walked out of school and went home without telling anyone. She phoned her husband who came home and called their family doctor.

Although at first it sounds quite similar, John's story is rather different. He was a little older than Susan, but he, too, became depressed over a period of weeks. He stayed at home and was visited by his family doctor who gave him antidepressant tablets. He seemed to be responding to this treatment, and his doctor was pleased with his progress.

At this time, John felt pretty good and quite enthusiastic about going back to his work as a telephone engineer. He rang up his personnel officer to arrange this. He told his wife that, as he was completely recovered, there was not much point in staying at home. When he got to work on his first day back, a certain number of relatively easy tasks had been set aside for him. He completed these very quickly and without difficulty, and felt very pleased with the way things had gone. He was pleased also to see his workmates, and rapidly overcame their slight awkwardness at having him back after 'a bit of mental trouble'. In fact, as he was feeling quite jokey, he soon had them all laughing and relaxed. His manager was also glad to have him back so obviously recovered.

Over the next two days John became convinced that one particular working practice, which previously he had put up with as a bit of a chore, was in fact grossly inefficient. He thought out how things actually should be done, and saw what a major change for the better it would be if this routine were brought in. He accordingly asked to see the manager who was somewhat taken aback when he found out why he had requested the interview. The manager raised a number of fairly obvious objections to John's proposal, although he acknowledged that it had some good points. John expounded his view fairly forcefully, and left feeling that the manager was more stupid than he had thought. He did not, however, let this blight his day. When he returned from work, he told his wife all about it.

In the evening he had a good idea. His car was almost due for a service: he would save himself money by doing it himself. He drove out and bought a large can of oil, and returned to the garage where he carried out an oil change. Although he knew in principle how to do this, he had never done it before and made rather a mess. However, this was a minor consideration compared with the sense of satisfaction with which he returned, rather dirty, to the house. His wife looked unsure when he said he proposed to service the car on a regular basis, and he felt she was unadventurous and a bit of a killjoy. She confirmed this opinion by going to bed at 11 o'clock. John did not fancy sleeping just yet, so he played some Mozart, music he had always been fond of. Tonight it seemed particularly pleasing. It was around four a.m. that the great idea struck him — no less than a completely new way of transmitting telephone messages. It was like a blinding light in its brilliant simplicity. He rummaged out a large and out-of-date diary, and began to put his ideas on paper as he was terrified they would leave him before he could get them down. His wife found him still scribbling when she came down in the morning. He said he was not going to work, as he had something important to work on at home. However, at ten a.m. he went out, and when he came back he told his wife that he had drawn money out of the bank to finance a business venture designed to develop and market his new telephone system. The enthusiastic and naïve way in which he talked about this led her to call the family doctor. John was not pleased to see her, as he was feeling very good indeed. His experiences would be regarded as typical of a bipolar manic depressive illness.

There is no doubt from the descriptions above that depression is a very unpleasant experience indeed. So, too, is mania sometimes, as the sufferer may feel very irritable and 'pressured'. However, John actually felt good with his illness and this can pose real problems, particularly if sufferers, while denying that they are ill, do things which they will later greatly regret. Getting such people to co-operate in treatment can be very difficult indeed.

Manic depressive disorders typically come on in separate **attacks**, and the patient is usually fairly well in between. Attacks may develop over a few days in either type, but sufferers from the unipolar condition often become depressed gradually over a period of weeks or months. Compared with physical illness, mental disorders do last quite a long time. Psychiatrists are used to this, but you, the relative, may not be. However, things have improved. Before effective treatment was available, attacks might last from six months to two years, but nowadays six months is usually the maximum, and many episodes are considerably shorter. Attacks of bipolar illness tend to be shorter than in the unipolar version, but may occur more frequently.

Many sufferers only have one attack of depression, but the majority do relapse. This is often after years of good health. Once a pattern of relapse has developed, the gap between attacks may tend to shorten, although this is not always the case. Some people may be persistently depressed, and this can cause great problems, as you will know if you live with them.

Negative symptoms (see p. 44) do occur in manic depressive illness, but much less commonly than in schizophrenia. Occasionally it may be difficult for the psychiatrist to decide whether someone is suffering from schizophrenia or manic depressive illness. This is less worrying than it sounds, for in borderline cases treatment is determined by the features of the illness rather than by its particular label. Sometimes these intermediate illnesses are called **schizoaffective disorder**. They are treated rather like schizophrenia, but behave more like manic depressive illness.

Causes
Severe mental illness seems to have no simple cause. It is often suggested that several factors work together to produce the illness. However, there are people who are subject to all these factors but never become mentally ill. Our knowledge of the origins of mental illness is a long way from being complete, despite years of effort and research.

Some mental illnesses **run in families** to a certain extent. This is true of both schizophrenia and manic depressive illness to a moderate and, indeed, roughly similar degree. The best evidence for this comes from the study of twins.

There are two sorts of twins, those that come from a single fertilised egg, and those that come from two separate eggs. The first sort are genetically identical, they share all the genetic instructions that determine our characteristics. The second type are really like ordinary brothers and sisters who happen to have been born at the same time; although they are closely related, on average they only share half their genetic instructions, so they are called non-identical twins. If these mental illnesses are genetically determined, you would expect the identical twin of someone with schizophrenia to have a much greater chance of developing the disorder than the non-identical twin of such a person. When groups of identical and of non-identical twins are compared, this is what is actually found. It means that the tendency to these illnesses is 'built in', at least partly. This may worry sufferers, and indeed may have worried you: where one person is affected there is a risk, usually small, that other members of the family may also develop the disease. This is an important topic, so we discuss it at some length on pp. 79–80.

Schizophrenia may sometimes also result from significant damage to the brain — what the medical profession in a nice piece of understatement calls a 'physical insult'.

Complications and difficulties during pregnancy and at birth are more common in babies who as adults develop schizophrenia. This probably means that in some cases **damage in the very early stages of life** may itself result in a tendency to the disease, although this does not appear until much later. We have no idea how this delayed reaction actually works in practice. In rare instances, schizophrenia can even follow a **physical cause in adult life** — a head injury, epilepsy, or certain uncommon bodily diseases. In most cases the connection is pretty clear because the physical condition produces its own symptoms by which it is readily recognised. Recognisable physical causes for manic depressive illness are also rare, but do occur, for instance in association with abnormalities of the endocrine glands.

Recently, some workers have claimed to have discovered

evidence that schizophrenia can be caused by a virus. In our view the argument for this as a major cause of the disorder these days is really very thin. In the 1920s and 1930s, the viral epidemic of encephalitis lethargica did indeed result in many cases of schizophrenia. Other infections have been associated with the features both of schizophrenia and of manic depressive illness. The most famous of these was syphilis of the brain, otherwise known as General Paresis of the Insane (GPI). Although this played havoc among the Victorians, eminent or otherwise, it is now so rare that we have only seen a handful of cases in our professional lives. It is almost unimaginable that your relative's illness is due to GPI, although the relevant blood tests are still carried out as a routine. Syphilis itself is now a rare disease and early treatment with antibiotics has effectively eliminated the slow progression to brain infection that used to follow it.

The evidence that both schizophrenia and manic depressive illness are associated with changes in various **transmitter substances** in the brain is now strong. The nerve cells in the brain form a sort of network, and work by switching each other on and off, something like the switches in a computer. One cell helps to switch on the next in line by giving out a chemical, or transmitter substance. The brain uses several of these substances in different places and, if they are not being released in the right quantities and the right places, it is believed that mental illness can result. We are even in a position to make reasonable guesses about which transmitters, and where. Quite a lot of evidence, for instance, suggests that in schizophrenia there is some abnormality in the handling of the transmitter substance **dopamine**, particularly in the connections between the deeper parts of the brain and the areas nearer the surface (the 'cerebral cortex') where the more intellectual functions of the mind, such as perception, thought and judgement, are carried out. Every drug that suppresses the action of dopamine also improves the clinical condition of someone with acute schizophrenic symptoms.

Another biological influence on these severe mental illnesses is that exerted by the body's hormonal state. It used to be thought that the menopause was associated with an increase in depressive illnesses in women. It is possible that this hormonal change may occasionally have an effect, but it cannot account for many cases. Much more important are the hormonal changes brought about by childbirth. These can lead to the so-called **post partum** ('after-delivery') psychoses, which can take the form of schizophrenia or of manic depressive illness, and often show features of both. It is relatively rare, occurring after only one pregnancy in 500. Sufferers rarely show negative symptoms (see p. 44), and there is a very good outcome for the attack itself. Further attacks occur following about one in five subsequent deliveries, and about half the sufferers have later attacks not associated with delivery. Hormones may also play a part in postnatal depression, a much milder, though still unpleasant, condition. There are, however, almost certainly social and psychological influences on this as well. There is a special Association for Post-Natal Illness.

Personality, which is a mixture of the temperament you are born with and the effects of subsequent experiences, may play some part in increasing the risk that someone will develop a mental illness. Attempts have been made to link schizophrenia with a particular personality type, the schizoid personality. Such people are aloof, sensitive, solitary and not good at making emotional contact. However, the evidence that they are especially prone to develop schizophrenia is not good. People who **behave** increasingly like this may indeed be showing the first signs of schizophrenia, but that is a rather different matter.

A number of personality types have been implicated in manic depressive illnesses. One is the 'cyclothymic' personality — people like this are moody, in the sense that sometimes they are energetic and enthusiastic and sometimes gloomy and lethargic. It is possible that it represents minor degrees of the mood swings that, if fully developed, would be called bipolar illness, so it is not surprising they sometimes make the move into a fully fledged illness. However, sometimes people who are persistently energetic and cheerful do surprise us by developing a 'nervous breakdown' — 'the last person you would have expected to have one'. This is the hypomanic personality, and people like that do indeed sometimes develop a severe depressive illness. Because those around them may be slow to recognise it, they may occasionally kill themselves before anyone realises the danger.

Another type of personality that often goes with a tendency to develop depressive illnesses is actually called the depressive personality. Some of this is probably the result of innate temperament, but people with this personality are most noticeable on account of their rather gloomy attitudes, which they have probably learned from their previous experience of life. They have a distorted view of themselves and the world which means that any new experience is interpreted in a gloomy and hopeless way. For such people, nothing good can ever happen because, if it did, they would not notice it or would find some way of devaluing it.

Finally, some people who are prone to depression are very obsessive and perfectionist. Because nothing is good enough for them, they can never feel good about things they have done. For most of us 'nobody's perfect' is a solace; for them it is a reproach.

In all probability, little can be done about basic temperament. However, recently therapists have made successful attempts to change the attitudes of individuals with a persistent depressive outlook using the techniques of **cognitive therapy** (see p. 133).

Both schizophrenia and manic depressive illness are also influenced by the **stresses and strains of everyday living**. Such stresses can take the form of some sudden misfortune or change in living circumstances, or of more enduring difficulties. Problems that most people manage to cope with seem to be able to push a few into mental illness, probably because of an existing tendency that way. However, such illness sometimes occurs without being preceded by any obvious stress, and this makes the experience even more incomprehensible and upsetting for the sufferer, friends and relatives.

At one time there was a theory that schizophrenia was the result of an abnormal family environment in childhood. The best known proponent of this idea in Britain is R. D. Laing. The research on this was never very good, and is now discounted by most scientists. It did have the frequent and unproductive effect of making the unhappy parents of those who later developed schizophrenia feel both guilty and defensive. It has also had a pervasive and unfortunate influence on the attitudes of some psychiatrists towards the parents of people with schizophrenia, which lingers even today.

Recently research has suggested that sufferers from schizophrenia are affected by tensions at home, but this is not very surprising and is hardly the same thing as claiming that the behaviour of parents can *cause* schizophrenia. It does carry the hope that relatives may be able to change things for the benefit of the sufferer, once they know how they might do this.

There has also been considerable research into the possibility that **diet**, **infections** or **allergic processes** may lie behind the development of severe mental illness. This research has not been very productive and it must be concluded that if these factors do have any effect, it is only in rare cases or to a minor extent.

This summary of our knowledge about the causes of these severe mental illnesses may lead you to think that the enormous effort put into research has not reaped much in the way of reward. This is not entirely true. We think that the slow progress has come about because these diseases are actually extremely complex and subtle. Indeed, if they were not like that, if they did not arise from very subtle imbalances in brain function, they probably would not show themselves so clearly and purely as mental diseases. Because of this, it seems rather unlikely that there will be any sudden break-through: research will find the answers gradually by piecing together what is almost certainly a very complicated jigsaw.

Outlook

Is there a cure for mental illness? There may be no clear answer to this question, either. There is certainly **no one cure** for the conditions we have been talking about, but then this is also true of chronic medical problems like rheumatoid arthritis. However, there are different sorts of treatment available that together can help relieve both schizophrenia and manic depressive illness, either wholly or in part. Treatment may take the form of drugs, ECT, individual psychotherapy aimed at helping the patient to cope more effectively, or the arrangement of the patient's life in less stressful and more productive patterns. Selecting the best combination of such treatments is often a complicated business that takes much thought on the part of the health professionals involved. We shall take you through these issues at much greater length in Chapter 4.

As we have suggested already, the outlook for mental illness varies: some attacks last for days, weeks or months; others, years or a lifetime. Even in the most prolonged conditions, there are variations in severity and periods when the sufferer is relatively well.

People who have suffered an attack of mania or depression usually get better, although as many as 10 per cent of those with the more severe forms do not. Although they may never have another attack, most will do so, usually after some years. Some sufferers, perhaps as many as 25 per cent, may have minor mood swings between attacks which can impair their efficiency. Attacks which come on gradually are likely to improve relatively slowly, and an illness that begins in later life has not such a good outlook. However, having someone in the family who also suffers from affective illness gives no clue as to outcome.

In general, the prospect for schizophrenia is less promising, but even here 10 per cent have only **a single attack** from which they recover completely. Only one person in ten is still in hospital five years after a first attack of schizophrenia. However, more than half the people who develop schizophrenia do suffer quite considerable **continuing disability**, or have repeated attacks, usually not doing so well in life as they otherwise might. By disability we mean here that the sufferer is unable to do enough — looking after themselves, working, socialising — to make as full and as happy a life as they might have done otherwise. Some may be quite disabled, occasionally to the extent that they have to stay permanently in hospital; these are, fortunately, a minority.

The prospect for schizophrenia is better for those who do not have a family history of schizophrenia. A relatively abrupt onset to the illness is also a good sign, particularly if it followed some kind of sudden stress. Negative symptoms (see p. 44) indicate a relatively bad outlook, mainly because they will probably persist when the acute symptoms have gone.

From what we have said above, you will gather that it is often impossible at the beginning of a severe mental illness to predict what is going to happen to someone. Professionals frequently avoid forthright opinions at this stage, mainly because they are frightened that what they say may turn out later to have been misleadingly optimistic or pessimistic. Your relative will be offered various treatments and these will affect the outcome in various ways and to a varying extent. Obviously, the sufferer's circumstances, reactions, and ability to manage will influence the success of the treatment he or she is given. Considerable time may be needed, however, and it can be months or even years before improvements become apparent. All psychiatric professionals work within this sort of time span. It can be confusing and unnerving for you and your sick relative to find that, unlike in physical illness, rapid improvements may not be expected.

Symptoms

We are now going to take you through the symptoms of schizophrenia and manic depressive illness.

Many of these you may immediately recognise from your own relative's behaviour. Others you will not know about, but we think it is useful both to learn what can happen to people's behaviour as a result of illness and to avoid being caught unawares by new developments. We shall concentrate particularly on those symptoms that are distressing, confusing or frequent.

Mental illness frequently shows itself through **changes in mood** even when this is not the central feature of the disorder. Normally most of us keep on a fairly even keel, although sometimes we may feel especially happy or a bit fed up. The mood of people with mental illness is much more extreme than most of us ever experience. We think this comes across in the story of Susan above.

People can be said to be depressed in mood when they remain sad, miserable, mournful or gloomy for days or weeks at a time, and when this mood **persists** despite all the efforts of themselves and those around them. One of the most characteristic symptoms is that the sufferer can no longer take pleasure in anything at all. Depressed people feel pessimistic and hopeless about themselves and the world, frequently **blaming themselves** for things that go wrong. They withdraw into themselves and do not talk much. Their energy goes, they are easily tired and they let things slide. In general, they cannot be bothered with things any more, and often lose interest in sex. They may feel so worthless that there is nothing left but to end things as quickly as possible, by an overdose or in a more violent manner. Those who do intend **suicide** will usually give some warning (see pp. 61–2).

In some people the loss of energy is very marked indeed. They move more slowly than they normally do, and often complain that they are walking as though they were twenty or thirty years older than they actually are. Sometimes, they may stop moving much at all, staying in bed most of the time. Occasionally they will develop an extreme condition, called depressive stupor. In this they do not talk or move, and may even become completely incontinent. This is very rare now, but was not uncommon in the days before effective treatment prevented things going so far.

Some depressed people become very **agitated**. They cannot keep still and often pace from room to room wringing their hands. They may continually ask their relatives and friends for reassurance — 'I'm not going mad, am I?' 'It will be all right, won't it?' This distress is painful to see and, if you have seen it, you will know that at the same time it can be extremely wearing.

Disturbed **sleep** is common in the mentally ill. Some people have trouble getting off to sleep, often because of depressing or worrying thoughts. Others sleep fitfully and restlessly. Some depressed people wake up in the early morning, a time they often feel at their worst. They lie there in anguish, feeling crushed beneath the weight of their sorrows. Those with mania can frequently manage with very little sleep, remaining very energetic into the small hours, and likewise waking early and refreshed. People who have been mentally ill for some time occasionally develop odd ways of living, waking at night and sleeping by day. This is usually part of a general tendency to avoid people.

Because depression makes people feel **physically run down**, they sometimes do not realise they are depressed, but think they must have some physical disease. Ordinary aches and pains become more noticeable. This may come out as fears of cancer or some other nasty condition, and occasionally leads to a preoccupation with physical health that can be very tiresome for relatives. Because bodily aspects are emphasised, the family doctor may not at first recognise the depression underlying the complaints, and may embark on unwarranted investigations and treatment. This mistake is easily made, and not uncommon.

Margaret was a woman in late middle age who began to

feel run down. At first she put this down to the fact that she was not as young as she used to be. She had always been a fastidious person of orderly habits, and she took more notice of an increasing tendency in herself to be constipated than other people might. What she did not realise was that constipation is not infrequent in depression, part of the general slowing that happens in moderately severe cases. She became very preoccupied with her bowels, so much so that she could not be bothered to go out socially any more. She began to notice pains in her stomach. She visited her family doctor who prescribed a laxative, without much effect. Her appetite declined. At this point, she read a newspaper story about a television star who had died of cancer. She did not tell anyone about this, but gradually came to the fearful realisation that her own symptoms were probably the result of cancer of the bowel. She was overwhelmed with anxiety which she bottled up for some time until at last she brought herself to return to her doctor. He took her seriously and referred her for investigations. This time he spotted that she was depressed, but thought it was a natural reaction to her fear of cancer. The investigations proved negative and the gastro-enterologist thought she was greatly exaggerating her symptoms, so he referred her to a psychiatrist colleague. She was fortunately able to identify the true nature of Margaret's problem.

In contrast, some mentally ill people become 'high'; what the psychiatrist calls **hypomanic** or **manic**. This is what happened to John. They are full of energy and ideas, and talk quickly and wittily. They race about getting things done (some of which are useful, some not). They may be found cleaning the cooker at four a.m., or may wake up the family at a similar time for an unplanned trip to the country. There is a danger they may seriously exhaust themselves and, indeed, in the days before we had adequate sedation, it was not uncommon for mania to cause death from exhaustion. They may get very **irritable** with those around them who try to impose a limit on their activity and their wild schemes.

They are often what the psychiatrist calls **disinhibited** — if they feel like doing or saying something, they will do so, without regard for consequences. This may be very hurtful. They frequently make new relationships with people they would not normally get on with. A few patients swing wildly from depression to elation in a manner that is very difficult indeed to cope with.

Some people may **lose their emotional responses** through mental illness, becoming wooden and unreactive, however hard you try to get through to them. This can happen with depressive illness, when someone is so frozen in her depressed mood that nothing seems to touch her. However, it is much more common and persistent in chronic schizophrenia where it may be the central feature of the condition. People's faces usually show a constantly changing pattern of emotions and expressions, something so normal we do not even think about it until we are surprised by its absence. However, in some cases of schizophrenia the facial expression is relatively fixed. This is unsettling. We feel unable to get through to the person any more, and he seems very unrewarding to be with, so much do we rely on facial expression for the feeling of being in contact with the other person.

Normally, it is possible to have an effect on someone else's mood. In particular, we can usually cheer up friends and relatives who are feeling down. One of the upsetting things about the change in mood which occurs in mental illness is that it does not seem to respond to our efforts, and certainly not to those of the ill person.

Another of the symptoms of severe mental illness is a belief in things that are wildly improbable or impossible. Other people's arguments or evidence fail to shift these ideas. Rigid and irrational beliefs of this sort are called **delusions**, and sufferers who act on them may get into a lot of difficulty and trouble with those around them. Some believe they are being **persecuted**, perhaps even by members of their own family. This may lead to arguments, and even fights. One man thought the IRA were leaving cars parked in particular places as a signal to him that they were on to him. Others, especially those who are manic, may have **unrealistically big ideas** about themselves and their abilities. This may lead them to spend money wildly or to develop grand schemes. They may even be able to persuade other people to take part in them. One man obtained a £10,000 loan from his ordinarily hard-headed bank manager to finance a completely cock-eyed business scheme.

Depressed people may be preoccupied with some imaginary wrong they have done, feeling horribly guilty. One elderly woman thought that she might have allowed a cannabis plant to grow in her garden and that the police were coming to take her away for trial and inevitable execution. Others may develop ideas that they are riddled with cancer or venereal disease.

People who have had delusions for some time may become wise to the fact that others quite obviously do not share them. Delusions may still make their behaviour unpredictable and hard to fathom, however, even if they do not talk about their beliefs. Some advice on coping with delusions is given on pp. 55–6.

Many schizophrenic and some manic depressive people imagine they hear things, often voices talking. This is an example of the sort of splitting we were describing earlier: products of the imagination are split off, so that they no longer appear as internal private experiences, but are projected on to the outside world. Sometimes, these imaginary voices may say things that upset the sufferer who may then act in a strange or violent way. They may shout back at the voices, go round to sort out neighbours who they think are making comments about them, or make complaints at the local police station. Hearing voices like this is usually a most unpleasant experience, although sometimes people get used to them and almost seem to take them in their stride. The psychiatrist calls these noises or voices

auditory hallucinations and puts considerable weight on them in diagnosing these severe mental conditions.

Hallucinations may also be of things seen, although this is more unusual. One man had visions of choirs of angels when he became manic, but when he was depressed he saw the most dreadful and excruciating torments of hell. Other sufferers, particularly those with schizophrenia, may smell or taste things that are not there. People experiencing such hallucinations may accuse relatives, neighbours or friends of trying to gas or poison them. One woman was convinced that the man in the flat above had built a pipe into her wall and was passing nerve gas into her sitting-room.

People may sometimes have hallucinations of touch. One unfortunate woman with schizophrenia felt hands going round her neck to strangle her as she walked down the street. Sometimes she would have some insight into this and be able to tell herself that the experience was unreal. At other times the power of the hallucination completely convinced her of its reality. This was very terrifying indeed, as you might imagine; she felt she was about to die and there was nothing she or anyone else could do about it. Other hallucinations may have a sexual aspect: people with schizophrenia may occasionally claim they have a phantom lover because of strange and unprovoked sexual sensations.

Schizophrenic people sometimes have other **odd experiences**. They may experience odd changes in their own thinking. They may feel that somehow their thoughts can flow out beyond the boundaries of their own head so that other people can pick them up and know what they are thinking. The flow of their thoughts may suddenly stop, leaving them puzzled by the odd sensation of a mind completely empty of thoughts. This can lead them to accuse people of taking away their thoughts, of 'scraping her brain' as one woman put it. They may also feel that some of the thoughts in their head do not belong to them, that they are completely alien, that they have been inserted or dropped into their heads from outside, like a stone into a pool. Others may feel that other people can interfere with or control what they are thinking or doing. One man thought the BBC had half of his brain on a computer and could program his thoughts and actions.

These experiences are so strange that it is quite hard for us to have any insight into what it must be like to have them. This again separates the sufferer with schizophrenia from the rest of us.

Schizophrenia and mania can both affect the ability to think straight in a sometimes spectacular way. The connection between thoughts becomes much less obvious, so that the sufferer's mind jumps from topic to topic in an unpredictable way. This usually reveals itself in disjointed speech. In mania, it may still be possible to follow the connections, although they might be ones we would never think of ourselves. Sometimes in schizophrenia there appears to be no connection at all between sentences, and in extreme cases the link between words in the same sentence may also vanish. This makes the sufferer's speech incomprehensible, as might be imagined. Disordered speech is most common in acute episodes of illness, but may also be seen in chronic schizophrenia.

One thing you may worry about particularly in connection with a mentally sick relative is the question of violent behaviour. **People who are mentally ill are, as a group, no more prone to violence than those who are not**. This is partly because mental illness often makes people **withdraw** from friends and relatives and become lethargic and apathetic. However, some sufferers, often those with schizophrenia or mania do behave violently while they are ill. Such violence is disturbing, as it is often unforeseen. There are three broad types of violence, any or all of which may be shown.

The first arises from the increased irritability of some mentally ill people — they are on a shorter fuse than normal. The violence is understandable, but is an excessive reaction to the situation. Such violence can be avoided if relatives and friends are aware that it may occur, notice when it is occurring, and change tack as a result. It is likely to happen when you have to refuse something your sick relative asks for, or disagree with what he or she says.

In the second type, the person strikes out unexpectedly at someone nearby. Afterwards, it is possible to see that the violent action was indeed provoked by the other person's action, but only because it was misinterpreted. It could not have been anticipated that the other person's behaviour would be so provocative. One schizophrenic man, Alan, had become preoccupied with the belief that his body was changing sex. A friend commented in a friendly way that he seemed to have put on a bit of weight recently and was surprised when Alan struck him. Alan had taken the comment as a confirmation of his worst fears.

The third type of violence is much rarer. It is planned by the sufferer, but arises because of **delusional beliefs** about his or her circumstances, and so is extremely difficult to predict. Sometimes the person gives warning, and obviously such warnings should be taken very seriously.

One man with schizophrenia had delusions of persecution, feeling that people were out to harm him. He kept these ideas to himself and his family was astonished when he made a murderous attack on a favourite uncle. It later turned out that he suspected his uncle of orchestrating the whole campaign against him.

Depressed people occasionally take sudden and unexpected violent actions. What usually happens is that the depression is so deep the sufferer sees no future for himself or his immediate family. Such people may kill relatives from a misplaced sense of pity. The newspapers occasionally carry stories of a mother who has murdered her children and then killed herself. However, such tragedies are fortunately very rare. They serve to illustrate that violence is sometimes a possibility when judgement is impaired by mental illness. Violence is always difficult to cope with, but we have provided some guidelines on pp. 67–73, in the hope that they will help those of you who are faced with it.

Some of the most difficult symptoms for relatives to come to terms with are the so-called '**negative**' **symptoms**. Some sufferers, usually those who have been ill for some time, 'lose' bits of their normal behaviour. They cannot concentrate for long, they lose interest, they have no 'get-up-and-go'. They may sit around listlessly, watching television, though taking in very little. They may lie in bed for long periods and avoid people. They may stop looking after themselves, becoming very untidy and rather careless about personal hygiene. Table manners deteriorate and other social graces may vanish. They lose the ability to react emotionally, seeming careless of people they used to be close to. They may seem to be less intelligent than before. At the same time they become stubborn. All in all, these so-called **negative** symptoms, almost invariably the consequence of prolonged schizophrenic illness, are among the most difficult burdens of relatives. This is partly because it is quite hard to see them as resulting from illness, rather than laziness, lack of feeling or even sheer bloody-mindedness.

Most mentally ill people are quite aware that something is wrong with the way they think and feel. However, in the more severe illnesses, **insight** can be lost. The sufferer cannot see that his beliefs are irrational, and may express the oddest ideas with considerable vehemence. If your sick relative is like this, you may sometimes have found yourself being steered into arguing with him or her, although you probably realised that this was quite pointless. However, when the belief is merely improbable (a Cypriot housewife in London believing she is being persecuted by the Palestine Liberation Front), relatives may occasionally find themselves wondering if there might not be some truth in what the sufferer says. Sometimes, if they are easily swayed, they may even act as if they, too, believe what the sufferer claims. One rather shy young man developed a severe depressive illness in which he believed that he had committed a rape on

a girl he had talked to on a couple of occasions about ten
years previously. He thought the police were going to come
for him and kill him. He managed to persuade his mother,
with whom he lived, that this might be true. The desk
sergeant at the local police station was surprised to receive a
call from her, asking to speak to 'George the exterminator'.

2 Coping with Mental Illness

The problems you may have to deal with
Some of you will be fortunate: your mentally ill relative will recover and the family will gradually get over the turmoil. If this does not happen or if your relative recovers but gets ill again in the future, then living with him or her may give rise to a variety of problems. As well as all the ordinary difficulties that families can face, there are extra ones, often unrecognised or poorly understood, that can arise because of a severe mental illness. The relatively new developments in **community care** mean that families are now expected to cope at home at an earlier stage in the illness than was the case 30 years ago. The average mental hospital stay is now only six weeks and well over 90 per cent of patients are discharged within a year. In some cases, in-patient hospital care is not felt necessary and sufferers remain at home all the time. Relatives often want to be involved in helping in recovery, and in providing continuing support if necessary. In the past, unfortunately, relatives often felt that they themselves were not helped, that their requests for advice were ignored, and that problems were not considered until a crisis emerged. We believe that this situation has arisen because health professionals have tended to see relatives as part of the environment of the patient, rather than as people with needs of their own. Happily, this state of affairs is gradually changing.

After-effects of the illness

There is still considerable confusion between problems caused by the illness itself and its possible unseen after-effects, and those caused by **other factors**, such as the sufferer's character and reaction to what has happened, or the effects of medication. Because of this, it can be extremely difficult for you to get the balance right, for instance between expecting too much of your relative and not expecting enough, or between allowing unreasonable behaviour to continue and blaming your relative for behaviour that he or she cannot control.

In one family, for instance, one son John, aged 21, had developed schizophrenia, and it was very difficult for the other members of the family, mother, successfully working brother and step-father, to know what to expect. He had already changed from an active teenager with a talent for art, into someone who was suspicious, sometimes violent, and very unwilling to get out of bed. When some of the more dramatic symptoms got better in hospital and he returned home, he was still very uninterested in doing anything, difficult to talk to, and liable to lie in bed all day. The family either tended to think that he had been prescribed too much medication, which meant they were angry with the hospital, or, less charitably, they said he was just lazy, and got very angry at him and at each other. In fact some of the loss of interest and tiredness seems not to have been due to medication or personality but to the illness itself. This is very common when someone has had schizophrenia. It took a long time for the family to realise this, and to understand that although John was responsible for some of his behaviour, some of it was beyond his control and he needed time and encouragement to become more active and more like his old self. In fact it took about a year and a lot of family effort for him to re-establish a routine and get himself a part-time job.

This is a complex issue and it often takes time to make the right adjustment. It may be a considerable while, as in

John's case, before some sufferers regain their former interest
in the outside world. Indeed, a few never seem to do this.
One mother described her daughter as 'losing her sparkle'.
The mother lived with her 30-year-old daughter Rachel. She
had been very worried at the changes in her daughter at the
start of her schizophrenic illness, as Rachel had a particular
idea that she looked unacceptable to the outside world, and
refused to go out. With hospital admission and treatment
this idea faded, and Rachel returned home and was able to
go out with her mother. However, she seemed to have lost
her enthusiasm and spontaneity, and unless her mother made
suggestions would stay indoors doing very little all day.
After some months some of the interest came back, but it
was a very gradual process.

A sick relative may also show much less in the way of
facial expression and affection for the family and be harder
to talk to. This can be both confusing and hurtful; it need
not mean, however, that a sufferer feels less deeply, just that
his feelings are not expressed in the same open way. One
father described it as 'you never know what they're thinking.
He sits there all day and you'd think he'd be bored; he
doesn't seem to be, but he never says.' In this family the
son, while retaining some odd ideas about others disliking
him, was able to go to a day centre, but was rather uncommunicative for most of the time. He would accept food and
laundry prepared for him, but answered in monosyllables
and never expressed gratitude or seemed at all curious about
his parents' viewpoint, or how they might have been upset
over his illness.

Another problem is **unpredictability**. There may be
some days when a patient is 'her old self' and then quite
suddenly 'I've lost her again'. These mood changes may
occur without warning, so that an ordinary conversation can
turn into a sudden series of accusations without apparent
reason. Severe mental illness can affect people like this, and
the individual is often not in control of strong feelings that
suddenly become convictions. It is usually best to be aware

that this sort of thing can happen and recognise it when it does. You should not feel that you have caused the switch of mood. The best strategy in the circumstances is normally to change the subject, distract the sufferer, or leave her for a while. One family, whenever their daughter started a tirade against 'the Russians', would offer to make a cup of tea instead of pursuing an argument.

The after-effects of a severe mental illness can include loss of energy, sleeping a lot, spending time doing nothing and wanting to avoid people. Although it may look like it, you should not be tempted to see this just as laziness and unfriendliness but try to understand that it *is* an after-effect. If a sick relative does nothing else *at all* but sit in her own room, this can be harmful. In such cases, she should be encouraged to go out, to join in with some other family activities (even if she says nothing), or to try attendance at a day centre if available. A certain amount of time spent by herself, even if she appears completely unoccupied, is not, however, surprising, and other family members should intrude on this gently and with caution. It is probably best to encourage a sufferer to participate, and to help with some household chores, without demanding that they be done instantly, or expecting too high a standard. Expectations can be gradually increased as the sufferer's competence and interest return. In Rachel's family, the mother started off on her return from hospital by asking her to help with some household chores — washing up, making her bed and so on — and she took Rachel out with her whenever she left the flat. Gradually Rachel began to do more for herself, and eventually would go shopping on her own.

Sometimes a lack of energy and a reluctance to be with people may lead sufferers to stay in bed of a morning. Relatives often find this difficult to deal with, being uncertain of the right approach. One mother found it useful and effective to offer cups of tea at regular intervals, together with a time check. She did *not* bring her daughter's breakfast, which remained on the table downstairs. Another mother adopted a more active approach. After calling her son several times, she would then go into his room if he had not got up by midmorning. She would laughingly ask, 'Head first or feet first?' and then physically pull him out of bed and on to the floor. He would then give in and get dressed.

Unacceptable or embarrassing behaviour

While families vary in their tolerance, there are several sorts of behaviour they are likely to find unacceptable. For example, sufferers may shout, swear or talk to themselves in a rather obvious manner, damage furniture or other objects or threaten to harm themselves or others. Obviously, you will want to control behaviour like this but you may feel unsure about the best way to do so, without causing worse arguments or upsetting your relative. You may feel that you get no advice on this problem from doctors or social workers: this is a common complaint. In all these circumstances, you should try to remain **calm**. Becoming upset or angry will make things worse. It can be helpful to remember that your relative is not and was not always like this, and may not be aware of exactly how hurtful or upsetting his or her behaviour is. Sufferers may well be reacting in this way because they are actually very **angry** or **frightened**. Waiting until a particular outburst is over, and then saying, 'I know you've been upset, what can I do to help?' has been found useful by others faced with this problem. It may be a good idea to leave the room, or to suggest that the sufferer goes to his own room or to another part of the house for a while. One sufferer would often talk and swear to himself. The family managed to limit this by making it a rule that it should only happen in his bedroom.

It is often a good idea, after a particularly upsetting or embarrassing event, for the whole family, including the sick person, to talk about it and work out ways of avoiding or limiting similar situations in the future. It is much better for all concerned if, when everyone is calm, you can make it clear to each other exactly what can be tolerated and what will not be, rather than leaving things unsaid and letting irritation and upset build up.

Peter was in his early thirties, and sometimes when severely ill he would take his clothes off, regardless of who else was in the room. His mother and married sister, who lived with him, asked later why he did this and told him how upsetting it was for them. Peter said that sometimes he felt he was told to undress as an act of penitence, but agreed eventually to do it in private whenever possible. He needed reminding, but this worked reasonably well and was easier than explaining his behaviour to visitors.

Coping with a depressed relative
If you live with someone who is mentally ill, maintaining the relationship while he or she is depressed can be one of the hardest things to manage. Depression saps the sufferer's will, and is quite capable of sapping yours, too. It can be particularly exasperating to see your best efforts to help come to nought, and it is not surprising that many relatives give up trying and withdraw, emotionally at any rate. This unfortunately reinforces the sufferer's sense of guilt and poor opinion of herself, and emphasises how isolating depression can be.

However, although it may often be difficult, demanding the patience of Job even, there *are* things you can do. The approach differs according to whether your relative is just becoming depressed, or whether the depression has really got a grip.

In the early stages of depression, it may be possible to improve things by using the sorts of approach that would be helpful for someone who was distressed or unhappy in the ordinary way. You may have to take the initiative, though, because depressed people find it very hard to confide. You can help by providing sympathy and sensible advice. For instance, if things at work are difficult, you may be able to see a way through the difficulties that your relative has missed, or persuade her to put them on one side until she is

in a better position to deal with them. You may be able to
provide practical support, reducing the load on your relative
by taking on some task or responsibility on a temporary
basis. One of the adverse effects of depression is to give the
sufferer a distorted view of matters, which in turn reinforces
the depression. By talking things through with her you may
be able to provide her with a healthier perspective.

Molly became depressed a few months after she had taken
on a temporary, part-time job in the cashier's department in
the local branch of a chain store. She was previously a
proficient and conscientious worker. She was not very
impressed by the efficiency of her colleagues or of their
working practices. However, when she became depressed
she saw these inefficiencies of others as overwhelming
difficulties, which she had to sort out in some way. She was
successfully treated with an antidepressant, and when she
was fully recovered she recalled how helpful it had been to
talk to her husband about the problems at work. He had
managed to get her to accept, at least with part of her mind,
that there was little point in getting upset about the working
practices of people who were her superiors, particularly as
she was only working temporarily and they had been doing
things in that way for a long while before she had joined the
company. Because they had a good relationship, he was even
able to poke a little gentle fun at her, getting her to smile
ruefully through her tears, as she saw things from his
viewpoint.

Reassurance is important to depressed people, but it must
not be offered in a crude way. It is not reassuring for
someone to have her fears and worries dismissed; it just
makes her feel that the other person has not understood, or
does not believe that her distress is real or valid. It is much
better to listen to the basis of the worries, to take them
seriously and to spot where the sufferer is being unrealistic
or oversensitive and put forward an alternative view. Your
interest and concern will also help to reassure her of what
she is very unsure of — that is, her worth.

When someone is depressed, people often feel they might try and take him out of himself. To this end they may suggest various social activities, or even a holiday. Unfortunately, this is often not a good idea, and in any case must be done very carefully. If it does not work and the sufferer does not enjoy the occasion, it may be brought home to him how impaired he is, and his depression may increase as a result. He may also feel guilty because he has spoilt things for others. Any social activity must therefore be planned in the light of the sufferer's state of mind. Simple visits by relatives or close friends may be all the sufferer can take and as much as he can benefit from.

If your efforts to get your relative over his depression do not succeed in a week or two, you should enlist medical help, at first through your family doctor, and if necessary you must press for psychiatric help. If your relative has had a depressive illness before, you may be quite a good judge of when things have gone too far, although it is often difficult to steer a course between tardiness and haste.

Even if your relative is getting assistance and medication from the professionals, there are still things you can do to help him. Indeed, it is important that you are not seen to give up in your attempts. Depressed people are rather unrewarding to be with, so there must always be a temptation for you to withdraw, and to a certain extent you may have to have time on your own, just to keep going. As a result of their doubts about, and poor opinion of, their worth, some depressed people can be rather clinging and dependent, and this can be quite difficult.

There comes a point when a depressed person cannot actually manage his responsibilities any more. When this has been reached, it is really up to you to take on these responsibilities yourself or organise others to do so. This means you must take charge and take over all household decisions without negotiation. Depressed people may be very **indecisive**. This may lead to long discussions about trivial matters that get nowhere because they continually change the basis of their argument. Such disputes are point-less, and you should avoid them or at least try and defer them. Sometimes sufferers may become very opinionated about family matters, and this can also lead to long argu-ments that fail to produce constructive solutions.

Taking over like this may make your depressed relative feel very guilty at the burden he is placing on you. You can manage this by explaining that it is only a temporary arrangement, that when he is better, but not before, you will expect him to take things on once again, and that he would help you in the same way if you were in his circum-stances. Depressed people feel safer if they can feel that someone has taken firm control of the situation. You need a certain skill to recognise the point at which you really have to take over. If you delay too long you may cause your relative a lot of unnecessary anguish. If you take over too early, you may be encouraging him to give up more than he has to.

In any case, even if you are doing most of the important things, you should still encourage your relative to do some-thing, even though it does not seem worth the trouble it causes you. Anne and her husband lived with her father Bob, who became depressed. Even though it was as much as he could manage, she still got him to dry the dishes. He could only do this very slowly and under close supervision, but Anne still thought it was important that he should do it. It gave her something to thank him for, and it allowed him the feeling of a task done. Another example of the use of simple activity to help someone who is depressed is given on p. 153.

If your relative has become so depressed that he cannot do anything at all, you must really consider whether he should not be in hospital. You certainly must not hide the situation from his doctor, indeed, you should make arrange-ments to discuss it with the doctor yourself.

In the vast majority of cases, depressed mood is temporary, so if you can last it out, things will get better.

Very occasionally depression may take the form of long-lasting misery that seems unaffected by treatment. This is very difficult indeed to live with, and sometimes the only way to manage is to arrange matters in less than ideal ways. This might include taking over your relative's responsibilities, not on a temporary, but on a permanent basis. It also requires that you deliberately protect yourself from your relative's misery at least for part of the time, by organising your life away from him to an extent. These courses of action will not do much to improve your relative's mood, but at least they may enable you to continue looking after him.

Coping with delusions

One of the most difficult problems you might have to face occurs when your sick relative has a fixed belief: e.g. 'The television is talking to me.' If you deny the truth of this belief, you may be seen to have joined the 'enemy'. If you go along with it, the belief becomes even more fixed in the sufferer's mind. You will find that **arguing** is **not** helpful. A useful strategy is for you to agree that the sufferer believes what he or she says, while making it clear that the experience is not real for you. 'I know you think the TV is talking to you; you are sensitive to that sort of thing at times; I don't find it talks to me', is one way of drawing a line for sufferers between their own reality and the outside world. Michael's wife could not at first understand what her husband was talking about when he said he was convinced that he had a special mission to fulfil. While agreeing with him and sympathising that he felt such urgency, she made it clear that it was not a belief she had, and that it was more important to her to have some help with a specific task (looking after their young son). This combination of sympathy (it is very important not to be dismissive) and distraction was successful some of the time in calming Michael and helping him not to act on his belief.

It is a good idea to discourage your relative from talking

about delusions to anyone and everyone. Sufferers can be told that, in general, they ought not to talk about such things to people who are not members of the immediate family. At the same time, if they do have a confidante outside the family, this can be a useful safety valve.

Restlessness, overactivity and anxiety

Some sufferers, particularly those with severe **depression**, can become extremely restless, uncomfortable and upset. They may be unable to sit still or to sleep, and spend hours pacing the room. No amount of reassurance seems to make any difference. You may well find this behaviour almost unbearable if it continues for long. It is nearly always helpful to acknowledge to your relative that he or she cannot feel very comfortable or happy or relaxed, either. Sometimes a walk outside together will be helpful; sometimes separate walks outside will be more so! Fortunately, symptoms of this type almost invariably get better as the illness recedes.

Pat, a mother of two in her forties, would sometimes feel unbearably anxious and upset, and ask constantly for reassurance that 'it was not her fault' and that she was not shouting obscenities. This was very difficult for her family to tolerate, as indeed it was for the staff when she went to hospital: reassurance did no more than help her temporarily, and the feelings could last for days at a time. The best solution seemed to be to offer a brief stock phrase of reassurance, rather than to spend a long time trying to comfort her, and again, to offer alternatives or distraction. Comments like 'we know how upset you are, try to sit down and watch TV/read the paper', seemed to be helpful while this distressing behaviour was at its height.

Effects on sexual relationships

Those of you who are married to or cohabiting with someone who becomes severely mentally ill will be concerned about **sexual aspects** of the relationship. While they are ill, many sufferers, particularly those with severe depression, will lose much of their sexual desire and interest. Some types of drug treatment also tend to reduce sexual interest. This, together with a loss of more general expressions of affection, can be particularly difficult for partners to understand or accept. When the illness improves, sexual and general interest will probably return. You may find, however, that the relationship has been changed in sexual and other ways, and that new patterns must be established. You may also find that your feelings have changed irrevocably, and feel that the partnership cannot survive. All the spouses we have talked to in this situation have wanted to end the relationship at one time or another, although the guilt this produces can be equally unbearable. Divorce is no longer uncommon in our society, and for some relationships a severe mental illness is a final strain that cannot be tolerated. Some couples, however, do find that such experiences draw them closer together than they have been before.

Mary and her husband Bill were in their fifties, but had not been married long. They found it very difficult at first to adjust when Bill developed a late onset type of schizophrenia. He had always had trouble staying in jobs, but this finally became much worse after a particularly damaging row with his boss, following which he refused to leave the house and was very disturbed. Eventually, after treatment in hospital, he returned home, and they had to decide how their relationship ought to continue. Mary's first impulse was to give up her career to 'look after Bill'. Bill did not want her to do this, and felt she would resent it in the long run. Eventually they decided that Mary should continue working part-time while Bill began to take on some of the domestic responsibilities instead of trying and failing at jobs. Bill's new role took some time to establish, but he began to enjoy it and gained a sense of achievement from having dinner ready for a tired spouse. Mary was actually very glad to relinquish the housework, and also to have time to spend with him on days when she was not at work. They both

finally described the relationship as very close, and as more
fulfilling, including sexually, in the way it had developed.

Promiscuity as a problem
Particularly if you are the parent of a daughter, you may be
worried by the **promiscuous behaviour** that develops in
some mentally ill people. A much loved child, who may
have been shy before the illness began, seems to lose
discrimination and chooses as sexual partners people who
would previously have been considered unlikely or unsuit-
able in some way. Sometimes you will feel particularly
concerned because she appears vulnerable to sexual advances,
and you might worry that outsiders could be taking advantage. This can be a very upsetting problem: you find that
your normal acceptance of an adult's desire for independence
and sexual freedom conflicts with your wish to protect a
loved child from sexual abuse or hurt. For adult sufferers,
there is rarely any way to enforce sexual rules. Even though
you dislike it, you may have to accept a certain amount of
independence and sexual freedom. The most useful approach
is to **support** your relative through these relationships,
showing you still care, despite her acting in ways you would
not choose her to. Help with **contraception** is usually
relevant and important, and you may be the person best able
to suggest and organise this.

Most families, particularly parents, find it very difficult to
accept this side of their relatives' adult life. The parents of
Mary, a woman in her early thirties, were distressed by her
going off for several nights with an unknown man, after
which she returned home dishevelled and uncommunicative.
They never did hear the full details of this episode. Thereafter
they tended to be rather protective of her, and discouraged
male friends from phoning or calling round. In this family
Mary herself was not worried by her lack of a boyfriend,
and she did not disagree with her parents' attitude. It can be
much more difficult if this becomes an area of dispute in

your family, and has to be sorted out in some way that respects your relative's adult needs.

In some cases, promiscuity may only be apparent for some of the time. This can happen in **mania** where it might be an early sign of relapse, and you may need to enlist urgent professional help. We give advice on how to do this on p. 63.

Diet

There is no good evidence that **dietary factors** can cause schizophrenia or manic depressive illness. Psychiatric disorders do result from deficiencies of **vitamins**, but these are quite different and, in addition, can often be recognised by their effects on your relative's physical health. However, many psychiatric patients do have poor appetites, and it is important for relatives to ensure as far as possible that they have **a good diet**, containing the essential nutrients.

Some sufferers **eat too much**, particularly as they may be rather underactive. In addition, individuals taking major tranquillisers, antidepressants, or lithium may be liable to put on weight. As with anyone else, it is not good for sufferers to get too fat. You should try and encourage your relative to lose weight, although this may not be very feasible in some cases, and may appear to be the least of the patient's problems. Sometimes the doctor may be able to change your relative to drugs which are less fattening, and it can be helpful to ask about this, if you think it is a problem.

Self-care

This is not a problem of everyone with these illnesses. However, for some people, the illness or its after-effects lead to a loss of interest in how they look, and how they look after themselves. In extreme cases, self-neglect may be severe, with the person not eating properly and living in squalor. This, however, is not usually allowed to happen if they live with a relative! Nevertheless, there are often day-to-day problems over bathing or shaving, and there may be

a difficulty about changing clothes, particularly underwear.
One mother described how her son became attached to a
particular set of clothes he had on and would not change
them. All she could do was persuade him to bathe about
once a month, and to wash these clothes while he was doing
so. When eventually they wore out, the same thing happened
to the new set. It is helpful in these circumstances to establish
family ground-rules for a *minimum* routine of bathing, laun-
dering, changing of sheets, that you can all at any rate
tolerate. Once a week may be a reasonable target, and, once
negotiated, your relative can be encouraged to stick to it. It
can be useful to decide on a particular convenient day and
include bathing as part of a general routine of getting up,
dressing and going out of the house. It may well need your
practical help to start off with, as shaving or hairwashing
may be particularly burdensome for a person feeling very
preoccupied or unwell.

Use of alcohol
While there is no intrinsic reason why a person who has had
a severe mental illness cannot drink alcohol, there may be
several reasons why it is inadvisable. First, anyone taking
drugs such as the major tranquillisers needs to be aware they
interact with alcohol. This can cause an **exaggeration** of
the normal effects of alcohol, and the individual may quickly
become sleepy, morose, or less in control of strong emotions
such as anger or fear.

Doctors normally recommend that anyone on psychiatric
drugs should drink very little alcohol, if any. However, this
may be quite unrealistic. Your relative may greatly resent
being given 'rules' about drinking, whether by professionals
or by you yourself, and may rightly feel that alcohol is the
only pleasure he now enjoys. In general, a couple of pints
of beer or two or three glasses of wine every other day
should not cause too many problems. As a rule of thumb,
your relative should try to think of his drugs as doubling
the potency of alcohol, so the effect of a pint of beer is likely

to equal that of two pints in former times. It may be that a little cautious experimenting is required. As with the rest of us, some mentally ill people have much more control over their alcohol consumption than others. Calm discussion about the problems excessive use of alcohol can cause for your relative and other members of the family is probably the best starting point. If alcohol is causing serious problems, the medical staff concerned with your relative's care should be told about it, in case he is not admitting these problems to them.

Some families, fortunately not a majority, find that worrying about a relative's alcohol consumption and his resulting behaviour can be one of the worst aspects of the illness. The sufferer may well not drink to what would normally be regarded as excess, but because even small amounts of alcohol can have effects when combined with drugs, the results of quite moderate drinking can be very unpleasant. John lived with his mother, and would nag and worry her every night for money for a few beers. He would consume these and then return home drunk and be sick over the bed. It took a lot of negotiation between John, his mother and the hospital staff before this pattern was changed, and John was able to behave in a more acceptable manner.

A different strategy was developed by Eric's mother. When Eric said he wanted a bottle of whisky, his mother would suggest that they both needed a drink and offer to buy one on her next shopping trip. She would do this, and for a few nights afterwards, they had a couple of drinks together. After that Eric lost interest, and the bottle remained half full in the cupboard

Threats of suicide

Schizophrenia and manic depressive illness are associated with a higher than average risk of attempted or actual **suicide**. Sometimes suicidal feelings may be a near-rational response to hopeless circumstances, but in other cases there may be no apparent cause. One of the reasons why a hospital admission may be suggested is to reduce the risk of suicide and help such feelings recede. It is sometimes when there has been some initial improvement that sufferers are most at risk. They may feel a bit more energetic, but still believe that they are a burden to others, that they have nothing to live for and that the future is completely bleak. It is not possible to prevent all suicide attempts: a determined individual can often be successful, even when under apparently close surveillance in a home, a hostel or a hospital ward. Fred, a depressed middle-aged man, was being monitored in hospital because he was regarded as a suicidal risk. He wanted to use the toilet, but while he was there, the nurse watching him was called briefly to a disturbance on the ward. Although he was only gone a moment, when he returned Fred had thrown himself from the toilet window, three floors up.

Threats of suicide can be very upsetting and difficult to deal with. It is commonly said that people who talk frequently about suicide never actually try to kill themselves. This is **not true, and all threats of suicide should be taken seriously**. It is true that patients sometimes make such threats for effect or because it is the only way they can communicate how distressed they are. At other times, they most certainly are seriously intent on killing themselves, and you may find it impossible to tell one kind of threat from another. It is sensible to take elementary **precautions**, such as not leaving tablets lying around the house and informing the hospital if the person seems more than normally tearful, morose or hopeless. You may find it helpful to ask your relative how he is feeling, as sometimes it is only necessary to notice the sadness and attempt to offer comfort and reassurance if it will be accepted. An arm round the shoulders or a cuddle may sometimes be easier than words, and often more effective.

Dealing with emergencies

It is in the nature of mental illness that you may sometimes be called upon to deal with urgent situations. The appropriate management of these depends on the exact circumstances.

Probably the most common situation is when you become aware that your relative is **relapsing** or rapidly deteriorating. It is always possible and often appropriate to seek the advice of your family doctor about this. You may be able to persuade your relative to make an appointment. It will be helpful if you can accompany her. Sometimes, she may decline to see your family doctor. This may be because she has particular fears about what may happen, for instance that she will have to go into hospital, perhaps never to come out. If she is reluctant, it is worth trying to find out what your relative feels about going to see the GP — you may be able to reassure her and get her to change her mind, particularly if you offer to go with her. If you are completely unable to get her to visit the surgery, it is reasonable for you to make an appointment and see the GP yourself. If you decide that this is necessary, there is plainly no point in doing it half-heartedly — you must put your doctor clearly in the picture. Otherwise, he may feel that you have just come for some reassurance. The GP may make a home visit if it seems reasonable to do so from what you tell him.

If your relative is currently attending a psychiatric outpatient department, the best procedure may be to consult the psychiatrist involved by phone. The psychiatrist may sometimes be in a position to reassure you. However, if a genuine crisis is developing, he will be able to suggest the best course of action, whether this is a temporary increase in medication, or even hospital admission. Sometimes your relative will be receiving visits from a **Community Psychiatric Nurse** who may know her better than the psychiatrist does. In these circumstances, it is reasonable to contact the nurse, who may decide to make an urgent visit to assess the situation. Some community nurses will routinely provide instructions about how best to contact them. In cases of doubt, the consultant psychiatrist's secretary will usually know how to get a message to them.

In some circumstances you may feel it is sufficient for your relative's next appointment to be brought forward. This can usually be done through the appointments secretary at the hospital.

Not all patients need to remain in contact with psychiatric outpatient services. It is usually appropriate for relatives of those showing signs of relapse or deterioration after a long period of good health to approach their family doctor. This is particularly so if they have moved house since last receiving treatment. Mental hospitals tend to have rigid **catchment areas**, and those who have moved outside the area of their previous hospital will come under the psychiatric services of their new area of residence. Under these circumstances, it is essential to proceed through the GP. Family doctors prefer patients to visit them in their surgery, as this is usually the most effective way for them to use their time. However, for some psychiatric patients this may be inappropriate, so it may sometimes be in order to ask your general practitioner to visit your relative at home. Sometimes, after seeing her, the GP may decide to arrange **hospital admission** immediately. Otherwise, an **outpatient appointment** to see a consultant in the new hospital may be arranged. If your relative is unwilling or unable to attend, or should be seen quickly, your family doctor may invite a consultant to visit her in the home (a **domiciliary visit**). Social Service Departments now have a legal duty to arrange for an assessment if a relative writes to the Director.

Occasionally, patients become very acutely disturbed. Where there are warning signs of this, it is obviously better to take action early rather than late. Sometimes, however, patients deteriorate very rapidly, and you may need to do something immediately. If you have a particularly good relationship with the hospital consultant, an admission can sometimes be arranged by contacting him or her directly.

Otherwise, it may be necessary to obtain the services of the family doctor who can assess the situation in the home and arrange a necessary admission accordingly. Sometimes, these relatively urgent situations arise when you and your relative are away from home. Under these circumstances, you may need to enlist the help of a local, temporary, GP, who in turn may arrange admission to a nearby hospital to start with. Your relative can then be transferred to her own local hospital when it is convenient and practicable.

In a few areas there are special **Crisis Intervention Centres**, where you can go to get help without necessarily contacting your family doctor. In a few psychiatric hospitals, for instance, the Maudsley Hospital, there are 24-hour walk-in emergency clinics, which will provide an initial assessment, offer advice and possibly arrange admission to a local hospital. You and your sick relative are likely to have to wait in an emergency clinic for some time before being seen, as they are run on a 'first come — first served' basis. It is probably not a good idea to go to a general hospital casualty department with a purely psychiatric problem.

Sometimes patients are so disturbed that they deny they have become unwell. In these circumstances, **compulsory admission** may be needed to prevent them from harming themselves or other people. This has to be arranged through the family doctor. Some details of the legal involvement of the relative in the procedures of compulsory admission are given in Chapter 5.

If a very disturbed patient leaves the house and the relative is seriously worried, it may be reasonable to inform the local police. They can act under the **1983 Mental Health Act**, or the Scottish or Northern Irish equivalents, to bring a person suffering from a mental illness, who is likely to be a danger to himself or others, to a **place of safety** (see p. 140).

The final emergency you may have to face arises from an attempt at **suicide** by your relative.

Most such attempts these days involve self-poisoning. Not all are equally serious, but you should seek medical help if there is **any possibility at all** that your relative could have swallowed more than the usual dose of a drug, or that she retains an intention to end her life. Some drugs, like paracetamol (Panadol), can be fatal after a delay, even though they appear to have no immediate effects. In the case of any overdose, you should seek general medical, rather than psychiatric, help. Family doctors usually do not have adequate facilities for dealing with overdosage, although they can help to assess the severity of the overdose and advise whether the patient needs to be taken to hospital. If there is any suspicion that the overdose might be a dangerous one, you should either take your relative to a **casualty department** or phone 999 for an **ambulance**.

Until the ambulance comes, you are in charge of the situation and this means that, at the very least, you must keep a **close watch**. After all, if your relative is conscious, it is possible she may intend to try again. If you do not already know, try to find out what she has taken, by asking and by checking the labels of any containers or bottles. A drink will help to dilute the poison and ease any damage to the stomach. Try water, milk or barley water. Do not give salt drinks: they are not very good at bringing on vomiting, and they can themselves act as a poison.

It is more important to get the patient to hospital as quickly as possible than to make her vomit. However, after she has been given a drink it may be reasonable to try and make her sick. **Only do this if your relative is conscious and co-operative**. Do **not** do it if the poison is a **corrosive** (bleach, strong acid or alkali). The way to induce vomiting is by rubbing the back of the throat, either with your fingers or with the blunt end of a spoon wrapped in a handkerchief.

When the ambulance arrives and you have a good idea what your relative has taken, make sure that the bottle or container goes to hospital with the patient. Label it and give it to the ambulance driver. If you have managed to make her vomit, you should try to get a sample of the vomit to send with the ambulance, again labelled, so that it can be analysed.

If your relative becomes unconscious, you must try and put her into the **recovery position** (see picture). This is because she may choke if you leave her on her back. Saliva or vomit could then flow back into the windpipe and block it, or her tongue could fall back and block her throat. If your relative is breathing with obvious difficulty, run your finger round the inside of her mouth to get out any obstruction (including false teeth). Then move her head gently back and keep it there so that the tongue is brought clear of the throat. Now turn her into the recovery position. Lying on her side in this way will keep the airway clear and allow any fluid in the mouth to flow out. Before placing your relative in this position, make sure there is nothing in her pockets that might be uncomfortable to lie on. Cover her loosely with a blanket or coat.

As apparently unconscious people may be able to hear, be careful what you say.

Never give anything by mouth to anyone who is unconscious. It may well choke her.

The recovery position is also advisable for people who are feeling faint, and essential for those who might suddenly become unconscious.

If your relative stops breathing, you must try artificial respiration if you know how to do this.

Coping with violent behaviour
We live in what is perhaps an increasingly violent society, but relatively few mentally ill people are in any way violent. It must be said, however, that the ones who are do get a lot of publicity. Nevertheless, despite its rarity, violence in the mentally ill does pose some rather special problems for the people who live with them.

The first thing to be acknowledged about violence is that, like suicide, it is not always preventable. There are some-times going to be situations when it erupts without anyone

The Recovery Position

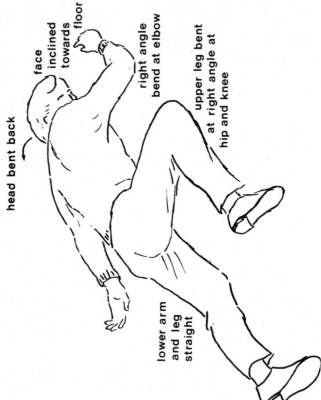

head bent back

face inclined towards floor

right angle bend at elbow

upper leg bent at right angle at hip and knee

lower arm and leg straight

being able to do anything to stop it. In the worst possible case, a pattern of repeated violence may be so established, for instance between a powerful son and his frail, ageing mother, that it is not possible to change it. In such cases, it may be necessary for the sufferer and his relative to stop living together, and even for the relative to take such actions as changing the locks or getting a court injunction against the offending person.

However, things are not usually as bad as that, and action can be taken to deal with the violent behaviour. This action has three aspects, depending on whether it is to do with anticipating the violence, deals with the act itself, or takes place in the aftermath.

Effective action taken before someone actually behaves aggressively is obviously to be preferred. If you know that your sick relative is particularly irritable and therefore in a mood that may lead to violence, you may be able to avoid triggering it. One way of doing this is **simple avoidance** — keep out of his way, go to another room, go out for a walk or to the cinema. Sometimes, you may have noticed that certain topics or situations tend to make your relative angry: obviously these should be avoided if possible. The strategy of avoidance can be quite effective, but it may have the drawback that nothing in the situation is changed, especially as it is not usually possible to keep the avoidance up for ever. One relative had learnt to recognise when tension was building up in her son from the expression on his face. When this happened, she would keep quiet and leave the room. However it was not always possible to stay out of the living room, as it disturbed the domestic routine of the rest of the family.

A somewhat more subtle policy is **deflection**: if tension seems to be building up in your relative it may be possible to defuse it by suggesting some simple routine activity, going to the shops or doing some household chore. This obviously requires sensitivity and good judgement, as the wrong choice may make the situation worse. Sometimes, relatives learn by experience that certain phrases are calming, and can be used to defuse the situation. One family would say, 'Why don't you go and have a lie down?' Sometimes this would work, but at other times the suggestion would be received angrily. It then worked better to say, 'Well, go out and buy *me* some cigarettes — here's the money — and come back when you feel calmer.'

A more direct approach is to confront your relative with his anger: this must be done **very gently**. One way of doing it is by saying in a quiet and neutral tone something like, 'I can see you are upset. Won't you tell me what's the matter?' This may sound trite, but at least it gives your relative the chance of talking about his angry feelings, rather than acting on them. Again, this requires very fine judgement, but it also carries the possibility of sorting the situation out in a more basic and complete way.

Sometimes your relative may become violent because he has misinterpreted things. This may be the sort of misinterpretation that any of us can make, but which those who are upset and distressed may make more easily, or it can be the result of delusional ideas. In either case, if you realise that your relative is becoming angry because of misinterpretation, you may be able to clarify the situation by gentle questioning. If the misinterpretation is not a delusional one, it may be possible for you to clear things up. If it is delusional, it may help to draw lines between your relative's reality and your own, in the manner suggested on p. 55. However far you can get with clarifying misinterpretations, it is important to keep the transaction quiet and calm, using a firm and unflustered voice. If you can give the impression that you are not going to become upset or angry, this will give your relative the feeling that things are under control, and this in turn will exert a calming influence. On some days one daughter would keep bursting in to her mother shouting threateningly, 'I know you're trying to kill me, why are you making me feel ill?' Her mother had learnt that one response that would calm her down was to say firmly but clearly,

'No, I was just sitting here reading the paper. Please don't shout.' It was often helpful to use distraction as well: 'Why don't we go out for a walk/make a cup of tea?'

Very often violence is a response to frustration — it arises when you feel you must refuse something your relative wants. This may happen sometimes anyway, but it is more likely if the ground-rules of your relationship have not been made very clear. So, for example, if you appear to have been inconsistent about what you think is all right and what not, violence may be the method your relative uses to get you to permit what you would really rather like to refuse. This underlines the importance of firmness and clarity in your relationship with someone who is mentally ill. He may be quite disturbed, but he will still be able to recognise this firmness and realise that there are limits beyond which he cannot pass. Knowing where he stands in this way may actually help him feel safer. Firmness in this sense is not to be confused with bossiness or intrusiveness. 'We agreed how much money you should have each day. I can't give you any more', said with conviction, confidently and consistently, when the previously agreed limit has been reached, is one example of the right sort of firmness.

However, consistency may be an ideal, but it is not all that easy to achieve, particularly if the situation has been going on for a long time and you have not been able to get help and guidance. If you have been inconsistent in the past, the pattern may sadly be impossible to modify. Inconsistency in one relative going hand in hand with violence in the other is a frequent cause of family break-up, although the relationship may stagger painfully on for a long time before this eventually happens. Usually, when there is a break-up, the well relative feels extremely guilty, even though the decision was the only realistic and practicable one to take. The relationship in our experience which most frequently gets locked into violence in this way is that between a mother, often elderly, and her ill but vigorous son: however, it can happen in most types of relationship, and we know of caring husbands who have been at their wits' end and indeed intimidated by their wife's violence.

You may be quite skilful at managing your relationship with your mentally ill relative, and yet there are still times when he becomes violent with you. It is just not possible to be completely in control of the situation all the time. After all, professional staff are hit and hurt by patients from time to time, and it can become a question of just being in the wrong place at the wrong time.

So how can you deal with the immediate threat or the fact of violence? It helps if you have thought out beforehand what you will do, and what you are prepared to do. It obviously depends to a major extent on how able you are to withstand an assault physically. The first principle is that immediately you become aware that you might be about to be attacked, you should avoid getting stuck in the corner of the room. Try and keep the furniture between you and your relative. Leave the room if necessary and if possible. If you cannot get out, as a last resort use a chair or a blanket or jacket as a defence. You may need to leave the house and call or phone for help. It may help to have made an arrangement with a neighbour beforehand. Do not be afraid to call the police if necessary.

Unfortunately, people like social workers or the police may not be able to do very much before violence has actually occurred. This seems crazy, but is of course the other side of our civil liberties in this country.

However, the police will often at least appear on the scene, and having several police officers around will frequently calm things down, even to the extent that when they have to leave, your relative does not become so angry again. This matter of calling the police does require judgement — if you get to the stage where your relative is continually having outbursts of rage and violence and you are continually calling in the police, this is no proper basis for your relationship. You must get outside advice urgently, preferably from a member of the psychiatric team involved in your relative's care, and if the circumstances cannot be changed for the better, you must seriously consider parting company.

Sometimes there may be no escape or possibility of help, and the threat of violence may be so immediate and dangerous that you have to comply with doing things you do not want to do. This is particularly the case if your relative has a knife or a gun, but also applies if he is much bigger and stronger than you.

If your relative has actually been violent towards you, hit you or whatever, it is important to try and deal with it afterwards in a way that may reduce its recurrence. It is relatively unusual to be badly hurt by a mentally ill relative. Being hit is, however, often very upsetting, even when the physical damage is slight, because it says something to you about your relationship, and also about the future — that it may be unpleasant, violent, and uncontrollable.

It is important that you should gently but firmly confront your relative with the fact that he has been violent and upset you. You should do this later, when he has had time to settle down — perhaps the next day. Most acts of violence occur in the evening or at night-time, and talking about it during daylight has a normalising effect. You should point out that you were hurt and upset by his behaviour — he may not realise the effect it has had on you. You should then try to get him to apologise: this emphasises to him that he has gone beyond acceptable limits. At the same time you should explore the incident and try to find out why it happened. Your relative may have been angry as a response to being very frightened, and your reassurance may be very helpful. He may also have felt that you were being unreasonable in some way. You may be able to explain the situation and your view of it to him in a way that is reassuring. It may then be possible to resolve your differences.

Finally, acts of violence often mean that your relative is relapsing, and this may require you to take further action (see p. 63).

Money problems

A few sufferers become very unrealistic about **money**, either during their illness or afterwards. This is particularly true of the **manic phases** of manic depressive illness, and some of you may know the illness is returning because your relative draws out large amounts of money from an account and goes on a spending spree. Other sufferers may not be able to get a job, and rely totally on social security or sickness benefit. They may find it impossible to budget, and demand extra money from you to pay for cigarettes, alcohol or daily necessities. You may find these demands difficult to refuse, but resent the fact that your relative cannot be more responsible or independent. Sometimes a **daily budget** can be organised, so that money is spaced out over the week and not spent all at once. Jane was able to agree with her mother that she should have £2 a day for herself. Clothing and other items were bought rarely, but out of their joint money. Gradually, as Jane became better at managing, it was possible to phase out this daily allowance system.

Husbands and wives of patients may find money problems particularly worrying. If the illness prevents the breadwinner from working, financial problems can indeed cause great hardship, particularly if there are young children. Sometimes it will be realistic for partners to **change roles**, so that the sufferer helps in the home while the other partner goes out to work. Often even simple household tasks will be too much for your relative, especially just after returning home from hospital, and other friends and relatives may have to help with child care and housework.

People sometimes fail to claim all the benefits to which they are entitled, and your relative may need your help in such matters. Benefits can be applied for directly at your local social security (DHSS) office, or you can send off forms available either there or at post offices.

Your relative may be entitled to a number of benefits. If he is unable to work because of his illness he is entitled to **sick pay** or **sick benefit** for up to six months and to **inval-**

idity benefit thereafter. Benefits will, however, be reduced if your relative is in hospital. **Mobility allowance**, payable to those who are virtually unable to walk if this is likely to last more than a year, is unlikely to apply to many sufferers from mental illness. Your relative may, however, qualify for **attendance allowance**, if you need to look after him or her during the day, or at night, or both, and you have already had to do this for six months. Indeed, you yourself might be entitled to **invalid care allowance** if your relative is receiving attendance allowance. **Severe disablement allowance** may be payable to those who are assessed as 80 per cent disabled and incapable of work. If your relative already gets attendance allowance, he would be regarded as 80 per cent disabled.

In addition, depending on outgoings, savings and income, you or your relative may be entitled to **supplementary benefit** or **housing benefits**. Your relative may be eligible for free prescriptions. If not, he or she may still be able to save by buying a pre-payment certificate. Under certain circumstances both you and your relative may be entitled to payments to cover travel costs to and from hospital.

In addition to the leaflets available at DHSS offices and Post Offices, help with money problems can be obtained from several sources. Most psychiatric hospitals have departments called **Patients' Affairs** or **Welfare Rights**. These are sometimes run by the NHS and sometimes by the local Citizens' Advice Bureau. Usually they deal only with the financial difficulties of **inpatients** and **day patients**, but in some hospitals they may be responsible for outpatients engaged in rehabilitation programmes. They will advise about entitlement to benefits and grants and will manage matters like payment of rent while the patient is in hospital. They are concerned with **statutory benefits**, not with grants from charities and the like. In some long stay hospitals, the department may offer a service limited to handling giro payments, but in such cases more extensive advice can be had at your local **Citizens' Advice Bureau**. Outpatients usually have to seek advice about benefits either from social workers or direct from the Citizens' Advice Bureau. Finally, there are various charitable bodies that may be able to help in particular circumstances and for particular purposes. They will often require the recommendation of a doctor.

Problems can be discussed with the **social worker** attached to the clinical team at the patient's hospital, or with one from the local social services department. Apart from benefit entitlement, social workers will be aware of other relevant services that, by taking some of the pressures off the family, may help it to maintain its income. Examples include a home help, a day nursery or play group, and occupation and leisure activities such as day-centres, workshops or clubs. The social worker will also know of any local organisations offering help to the mentally ill or their relatives.

If you have no contact with local authority social workers, it is always worth ringing the local department (the number will be in the phone book under the County or Borough Council). Ask to speak to the social worker 'on duty'. A brief description of your circumstances should be enough to enable the social worker to decide whether it is worth coming to the office for an appointment.

The doctors or nurses involved in the care of your relative will explain the best way to get in touch with the hospital social worker, and are likely to suggest this course of action in any case.

What can be done if your relative cannot manage their affairs because of mental illness?
If you are worried because your relative seems to be getting into difficulties in managing money or property, you may suggest to her that she takes out a Power of Attorney authorising you or another person to handle her property. This is a legal document which your solicitor will help you with. It depends on your relative being able to understand what is meant by signing the document, and if she afterwards

becomes mentally incapable, the power is revoked. She may also revoke it herself at any time. If your relative is so mentally disordered that her power of attorney would be invalid, you can apply to the **Court of Protection**. This is part of the Supreme Court and is staffed by judges. The address is given in the Appendix, and the Court itself will advise you about the correct procedure. It will assess the medical evidence and may appoint a **Receiver**. The Receiver may be a court official but is usually a relative or close friend. He has control over the patient's property, and duties such as investing money, settling debts and keeping property in good repair. The Court can also conduct legal business for the patient, such as divorce proceedings or making a will. Unlike an ordinary Power of Attorney, the patient cannot revoke this arrangement. Patients must be told of an application to the Court of Protection, and can object if they think it is unreasonable. They must then write to the Court within seven days of being informed or before the hearing, whichever is the later. They may provide their own medical witnesses to their fitness.

The affairs of an individual that have been taken over by the Court are examined from time to time by officers appointed by the Lord Chancellor. These **Lord Chancellor's Visitors** have the duty to see that things are being managed properly and for the patient's benefit. If you are not the Receiver, and are worried that your relative's affairs are not being properly handled, you should consider writing yourself to the Court of Protection.

The Court of Protection does have a duty to be cautious. In our experience, this can sometimes make it a rather inflexible and bureaucratic organisation. For this reason, it is best to invoke its help only when it has become absolutely necessary, as it may later make decisions which you cannot change and would not have wished.

Children in the family

You may worry that other members of the family, especially your sick relative's children, will be adversely affected by the strain of living with someone suffering a severe mental illness. It is, of course, impossible to rule this out, particularly if the illness leads to financial or other hardships, or to upsets like having to move house or change schools frequently. However, many children have to cope with these things regardless of their parent's mental health. Getting help from neighbours, friends and other relatives may be crucial in relieving strains, and will mean that children have other adults to turn to if required. Some reasonable and simple explanation should always be given even to younger children. Confusing messages about 'Daddy going away', without any reason being given, can make children feel insecure and upset, or even that in some way it is their fault. It may be helpful to talk to children in a period of calm about some of the experiences that the parent has when he is ill. The experiences can be compared to being in a dream, not necessarily a pleasant one, that continues even when the parent is awake. This can be used to explain why the parent may be preoccupied or upset, or seem less caring or interested in the child. Older children can themselves often be supportive, if they are given a chance to understand the problems, and difficulties are dealt with calmly so that upsetting or frightening crises can be avoided. If problems do become too difficult, families with dependent children will normally be given prompt help from professionals, such as the local social services department, child guidance clinic, or the hospital team dealing with the adult patient.

Occasionally problems in the family where there are children may seem insurmountable. In these circumstances, the local authority social services department or hospital social worker may well be able to help. Their aim will always be to try and prevent the children from leaving their family home, and they may be able to offer domestic help or a substitute carer who lives in while a parent is in hospital, or while a parent is at work. In exceptional circumstances children may be temporarily received into the care of the local authority and placed with foster parents or in a children's home. This would only occur if there was no familiar alternative person, such as another relative or friend, who was able and suitable to care for them. The local authority can pay temporary carers if there are financial difficulties.

Another worry that affects families is the possibility that children may **inherit** the tendency to the disorder. This risk is real, but differs according to the exact circumstances. The worst situation is very unusual, and is when both parents have schizophrenia. In this case, around half of the children will be affected by the disease. Normally, only one parent has schizophrenia. Overall, the risk that a child with one affected and one unaffected parent will also develop schizophrenia is about 10 per cent, but this varies, depending on a number of factors. It is less when the schizophrenia in the parent is associated with a recognisable non-inherited cause, like **birth injury** or, later on, **head injury** or **epilepsy**. It is also less if no one else in the family has the disease. The risk is greater when the parent's schizophrenia is of a severe type.

Manic depressive illness, particularly the bipolar type, also runs in families. For bipolar and severe unipolar illnesses this is mainly because it is inherited, not because people in families tend to share troubles and difficulties that might cause depression. The inherited risk for bipolar disorder is probably about the same as for schizophrenia, that for unipolar disorder a bit less.

The fact that these disorders are partly inherited raises the question of whether people who develop them should choose to have children if they have not already done so. Most professionals would feel that the genetic risk in the majority of cases is of a degree that should not necessarily deter possible parents. Obviously this is a decision that must be taken by the couple, and the genetic risk is only one consideration. More important is whether the illness seriously undermines the sufferer's ability to carry out the duties and everyday responsibilities of parenthood.

Finally, there is no reason why the unaffected brothers and sisters of a person with one of these conditions should not themselves have children: here the genetic risk is very small indeed.

In some centres, it is possible to get advice on these matters from a special **Genetic Counselling Service**. It may be worth asking if there is one in your area.

Relapse

In most cases, particularly if relapse (a recurrence of the illness) has occurred before, you will be the best judge of whether your relative is becoming ill again. However, some pointers may be useful, as these illnesses often do follow a relapsing course and sometimes the development of the relapse may not closely resemble the original form of the illness.

Relapses are recognised by changes in behaviour. One of the problems in spotting the early stages of relapse is that the changes often happen gradually. This means that it may be very difficult to distinguish between normal behaviour and that due to the illness developing again.

For example, one of the changes that occur in **mania** is increased **irritability**. If someone loses his or her temper, it is often hard to tell if this is a normal response, or a bit excessive for that person in these particular circumstances. This is the sort of judgement you are liable to be extremely good at as you live with the person all the time. Indeed, one of the common complaints that you may level at clinical staff is that they do not believe that you can pick up such subtle changes, and so do not act upon the information, thus failing to prevent a crisis from developing.

What symptoms should you look out for? In **schizophrenia**, changes in sleep pattern and appetite can give a clue. The sufferer may stay up into the small hours of the morning, sometimes compensating by rising at a later time.

He may go off his food, or eat in a more faddy way. He may spend increasing amounts of time on his own, shying away from the company of the family or of visitors. He may not look after himself so well and behave in awkward or obstinate ways. He may be increasingly suspicious and wary. A chance remark may suggest that he is returning to the preoccupations he had when he was ill. One wife knew that her husband was relapsing when he lost interest in going to the day centre, spent more and more time in bed, and began talking again of 'the Russians' on the TV programmes. In many people with schizophrenia, relapse is heralded by the sorts of feelings of tenseness and nervousness that we all experience from time to time, but which in them may mean something more sinister.

The major changes may be of **mood**: they may be increasingly nervous or depressed. However, people with schizophrenia sometimes become depressed without it indicating relapse: they often have enough to be depressed about, so it may be hard to distinguish these reactions to their unrewarding situation from the symptoms of relapse.

Relapse in **unipolar depression** is often gradual. The person slowly becomes less energetic, doing less about the house. She loses pleasure in things that usually please her. She becomes quieter and less sociable. She may have trouble getting off to sleep or wake much too early in the morning. She takes less pleasure in eating and may eat less, leaving food on the plate. The sufferer may surprise you by bursting into tears in response to what seemed a fairly harmless remark.

In contrast, the return of **mania** may be suggested by an increased energy. The person becomes noticeably more jovial, and may start to make plans or organise things. The husband of one sufferer knew she was relapsing when she took over the task of walking the dog and began to make slightly unrealistic plans for a return to work. Your relative may begin to stay up late and be more talkative than usual.

She may eat more and hurry her food. She may also become more irritable.

If you think your relative is relapsing, you must take action. Some guidance is given on p. 63.

All the changes described above can be seen in a fully fledged relapse. In the early stages, they are much less pronounced. This makes a real problem for you. On the one hand, if you can recognise a relapse early, it can be nipped in the bud by prompt treatment. On the other, it makes a relationship difficult if you are always on the alert for signs of relapse, and everything your relative does is evaluated to see if it is normal or might be the effect of illness. Obviously a balance has to be struck, and you will have to reach this in the light of your own particular experiences.

It is also possible that if your relative starts refusing to take his medication, a relapse will become more likely over the next few months. This is a problem looked at in more detail under treatments in Chapter 4.

3   Services

The people involved in the care of your relative
These days, psychiatric services are usually organised in
multidisciplinary teams. Although these are led by a
consultant psychiatrist, considerable responsibility is given
to each member. You may meet several of them, as the team
may select two or three people who will become involved
in the care of your sick relative. They may be from any
discipline — a nurse, a social worker, an occupational therapist — depending on your relative's particular problems, so
it may sometimes seem as though 'the doctor' never sees the
sufferer. The team does meet regularly to discuss the
progress of each patient, so that everyone on it should know
what is happening. However, patients sometimes feel that
although they were 'under Doctor Smith', they were only
seen once or twice, so the doctor could not have known
much about them. If the team is working properly, this
will not be true because each member will keep the others
informed. The main advantage of this team approach is that
the patient is seen as a whole person, who may have needs
that are best satisfied by a particular member of the team,
not necessarily a psychiatrist. It also means that you do not
have to rely on only one member of staff, who may be
unavailable or with whom you may disagree. The disadvantage is that you may feel you never get to talk to the same
person, and sometimes none of them may seem to know
what is happening! This can be a real problem, particularly

in a crisis, but a good team will try not to let it happen often.

Although many people do not realise this, **psychiatrists** have to train as ordinary medical doctors first. This takes five or six years. In this country, they then have to undertake a further six years or so of training in psychiatry. After about three years of this time, they will sit the entrance examination for membership of the **Royal College of Psychiatrists**. If they pass, they are entitled to put 'MRCPsych' after their names, initials you may have seen, for instance, in correspondence. After a further period of supervised work, they may apply for posts as consultants.

Clearly, this is a long training; sad to say, even these days patients and their relatives sometimes feel it must have missed the point, creating a psychiatrist who may not appear very good at offering support and information.

Consultants are assisted by more junior doctors part of the way through their training: **Senior Registrars**, **Registrars** and **Housemen**. Senior Registrars are also usually members of the Royal College.

One popular image of psychiatrists, perhaps the most popular one, is of someone very powerful who behaves rather oddly and has an uncanny ability to see into the deep recesses of the mind. The truth is more down to earth. A good psychiatrist may have insights into a situation that you may not have thought of, but this comes from long experience and an objective alertness to all the possibilities. The psychiatrist needs information to do this, and this is why assessment involves so many questions (see p. 91). They may be better at detecting false information than untrained people, but they are still far from infallible. One of us (Paul) is a consultant psychiatrist:

I work with a team on a general psychiatric ward. The team also has a senior registrar and a registrar. The senior registrar is shared with the other two consultants who have beds on the ward. There are several nurses of various grades and a community psychiatric nurse. I also have the assistance of the occupational therapy, psychology, and social work departments, although they are not often represented at ward rounds because of shortage of staff. As I am primarily a research worker, I devote only two sessions to this National Health Service work. One of these is a **ward round** and one a clinic in which I follow up those of my patients who have particularly difficult problems or who are likely to need to see me for a long time. The term 'ward round' is borrowed from general medicine, where the consultant actually does go round the ward with the team, seeing each patient in bed. In psychiatry, the ward round is much more like a staff meeting, which takes place in a special room (see also p. 93). People with fairly severe episodes of mental disorder are admitted to the ward, where they are assessed by the various members of the team. In the ward round, I hear about these new patients, see them, and help the team come to conclusions about diagnosis, treatment and management that will best help the patient. In this I operate a bit like the chairman of a committee, summing up the consensus view of my colleagues. In theory, as responsible medical officer, I have the final word in medical matters, but decisions are almost always by joint agreement.

I also hear about the progress of patients admitted earlier, but do not have time to see more than a few of them each week. However, I do see them at times when important decisions have to be made, for instance, about discharge or an application for a hostel place. Clearly, none of the day-to-day running of the ward is done by me but we have a 'management' period at the end of the ward round at which any particular problems are ironed out. Sometimes I see the patients' relatives, although that is also done by other members of the team. Some of my time is used to teach and supervise my junior colleagues, who on their own treat most of the outpatients seen by the team. This is an efficient way of use of limited resources. This pattern of working is a common one, repeated in wards and clinics throughout Britain. A few consultants run outpatient clinics in general practice health centres, a trend which is likely to increase.

Nurses are also organised in various grades. The head nurse in a ward is a **Charge Nurse**. After psychiatric training lasting three years, nurses become **Registered Mental Nurses** (RMN). Some mental nurses are also **State Registered Nurses** (SRN) or **State Enrolled Nurses** (SEN), that is, they have a general nursing qualification, and some, particularly these days, have taken degrees in nursing. There are plans to discontinue the category of SEN.

Most mental nurses work in hospital wards and clinics. Of increasing importance, however, are nurses who spend most of their time visiting patients in their homes, **Community Psychiatric Nurses** (CPNs). They have all had long experience of psychiatric nursing, usually as Charge Nurses. They will also have undertaken a one-year training course in community psychiatry. Such nurses usually have their base in a hospital, but some work directly with family doctors. They may be closely involved in the treatment of people who have been discharged from hospital following serious episodes of mental illness. They keep an eye on the patient's medication and may give injections. They monitor the general situation of the patient and the family, and provide a significant source of advice and support. They also keep the consultant and the psychiatric team informed of progress, so they form an important channel of communication.

John has been a community psychiatric nurse for about three years. During most of this time he has been visiting Phil, a young man about his own age who suffers from schizophrenia. Phil has been reasonably well, and able to live at home with his parents. There are rarely any problems, but sometimes Phil's parents like to be able to talk things over with John, which he is always ready to do. Indeed he has become something of a friend to all the family. He also gives Phil a long-lasting injection every three weeks. Recently Phil began to experience a return of some disturbing symptoms but, with John's help, he and his family were able to cope with this and things settled down again. The enduring relationship that has developed between John and Phil and his family is a good example of the valuable part played by many community psychiatric nurses.

Social workers have a considerable role in psychiatry. They may be involved with individual patients, offering **support** and **counselling**, and using a range of techniques aimed at improving the patient's ability to cope. They also have **expert knowledge** about welfare rights, practical aids and community facilities. They have particular powers and duties under the **Mental Health Act** and other legislation. Some social workers are based in local authority offices, others in psychiatric hospital services.

In the 1970s, most social workers did not specialise in any particular area of the various duties of their profession, but this has changed because those who carry out functions under the new Mental Health Act must now have additional training and be approved by a local authority. At the moment, the quality of training does, unfortunately, vary in different local authorities because each authority differs in its policy and in its involvement in mental health work. Each local authority does, however, require to have its training programme authorised by the Central Council for Education and Training in Social Work.

Like CPNs, social workers often provide help and support for mentally ill people and their families over a long period, and may do this by visiting them in their homes. Social workers frequently get a bad press, but they are often unconsciously and unfairly blamed for the very problems they are trying to alleviate. Sometimes these problems are not likely to go away, and the aim of the social worker may be merely to make them a little more bearable. They are then blamed for failing to do the impossible and accused of 'doing nothing'. Clearly, as with any other profession, not all social workers are equally competent. Nevertheless, many give excellent and determined support to people with great and enduring difficulties. Many social workers have a particular interest in the difficulties that families experience, and may spend a lot of time visiting the homes of patients. They should have a knowledge of what is available in the community to help the mentally ill. Advice on how to obtain the help of a social worker is given on pp. 76 and 101.

Clinical psychologists have a degree in psychology, following which they undergo a further two or three years of clinical training. Some have also done another research-based degree after a period of research (a PhD) and are then called 'Doctor', so this title is not confined to those with medical training. You may perhaps have been confused by this, not being sure if the person you are talking to is a doctor of the medical sort or of the research sort.

Clinical psychologists specialise in **assessing** and **treating** behavioural problems. They also have an interest in **measuring** and **evaluating** patients' progress. Clinical psychology is still a small profession. Its members are normally based in mental hospitals, but some now work in community health centres. One of us (Liz) is a principal clinical psychologist:

> I work with a multidisciplinary team which specialises in offering long-term care to the adult mentally ill, most of whom have been in contact with hospital services for many years, but now live in the community with varying degrees of professional and family support. The team consists of all the disciplines just described and together we attempt to assess and manage the various problems and crises that arise. These may be mundane, such as how to get a physical illness seen to or obtain a bus pass, or dramatic, such as taking someone into

hospital because they have just tried to kill themselves. We have a considerable number of activities that we can offer to people on the site — workshops, adult education classes, patient groups, and individual and family counselling. Many patients just drop in to pick up their regular supplies of medication, or to have a talk with members of staff and with other patients. Medication is regularly reviewed, along with the other problems that our clients may have. As a psychologist on the team (although only working part-time), I concentrate on offering advice about specific problems, such as violence or poor self-care, or being frightened of travelling. I help other staff to devise programmes that enable the team to evaluate how individual patients are getting on, as I have an interest in assessing and monitoring patients' progress. Psychologists do not administer drug treatments, but concentrate on the non-physical treatments (see p. 127), talking over and planning in detail how to approach and sort out a problem, and then evaluating what was useful.

I have a research interest in offering help to relatives who look after a mentally ill family member, and see families at home. I have also run a relatives' group. I encourage other staff to be supportive to the relatives of our patients, and advise them of the best ways of doing this.

In medicine as a whole, there are a number of **remedial** professions, which include physiotherapy and speech therapy. Within psychiatry, **occupational therapy** is by far the most prominent of these. Occupational therapists undergo a three-year course of training. Their job is to design and carry out programmes of activities intended to **overcome handicaps** and to foster or maintain **personal functioning**. These programmes may be based in the hospital ward or in the Occupational Therapy department. Some occupational therapists are now based in the community.

The work of the occupational therapist is described in more detail on p. 128.

There is in practice a lot of overlap in what members of these professions do when they see patients. Much of the assessment and treatment of psychiatric disorders is carried out by getting to know patients and by talking to them over a considerable period. Each profession does have its own particular specialist knowledge as well, and only psychiatrists, because of their medical qualification, are able to prescribe drugs. Psychiatric services are usually organised in teams because this is a good way to use the different contributions that each profession can make. Occasionally there are disadvantages. If the team is badly organised, there may be failures of communication. Each member of the team may think that someone else is dealing with a particular problem, when in fact no one is. If there is a possibility that this has happened in the case of your relative, you should raise the matter with the person on the team you have had most contact with. However, a good team can sometimes be of great assistance to you and your relative.

The services available to your relative
For most people who become mentally ill, the professional they see first is the **General Practitioner** (GP), sometimes called the family practitioner or family doctor. They will usually be seen, by appointment or 'on spec', in the GP's surgery, although sometimes GPs will make a home visit if a surgery appointment is not feasible. They normally deal with minor cases themselves, but will **refer** more serious conditions to the psychiatrist. The usual procedure is to make an outpatient appointment. This will in most cases take place at your local general or psychiatric hospital, although a few psychiatrists have sessions in health centres. If an appointment is made for your mentally ill relative, you should be aware that there is likely to be some delay, a few weeks perhaps, before he or she is seen. Psychiatrists like their patients to be accompanied to appointments, partly so

that they have a further source of information if they need it. Do not be reticent about asking to see the psychiatrist if he does not himself suggest it, or about seeking answers to your queries. Your relative may have to wait for some time, particularly if she is seen first by the registrar who will then discuss things with the consultant. Going with her to the appointment will give her some company while she waits, and this may be especially appreciated if she feels apprehensive about it.

Sometimes more urgent action seems necessary, and the GP will arrange for a **domiciliary** visit whereby the psychiatrist will come to your home and assess your relative there. This can be arranged within a few days.

Psychiatrists **assess** patients largely by collecting information, both from the ill person herself and from her relatives, and even occasionally from other acquaintances. They do this in order to discover what form the illness takes, what sort of person the sufferer normally is, and what stresses and strains she has been exposed to. The psychiatrist will usually obtain information about your sick relative's symptoms directly from her, but may back this up by getting an account from you or other members of the family. A patient's relatives will often be the best people to describe the way the illness has developed. In addition, the psychiatrist will gather background information that provides the overall context within which to understand the origins of the disorder. This means they may well have information provided by your family doctor, and from local authority social workers if they have been involved. Sometimes, this background information will be gathered by the social worker on the team who will interview you separately. Obviously, it is very important that the information you give to members of the psychiatric team is true, and as full as possible. Sometimes, you may feel that a question is irrelevant or intrusive. It is then possible you would prefer not to answer it fully. However covering things up in this way may hinder the clinical staff from helping your relative.

Very occasionally, schizophrenia or manic depressive illness can be mimicked by bodily diseases. The psychiatrist may order blood tests or other investigations to exclude these, either as a routine or as a result of symptoms that suggest they are appropriate.

After the psychiatrist has assessed the patient, the GP will often carry on the treatment of minor conditions. More serious problems may involve regular outpatient attendance. However, a patient will sometimes need to be admitted to hospital.

Psychiatric wards are likely to be one of **three types**. Your area may have a psychiatric admission ward in the **District General Hospital**. These are not usually far away. They are often bright, modern and purpose-built, but sometimes they may be an awkwardly placed ward that was originally built for some other purpose and later adapted. Other areas have their admission wards in an old-style **Mental Hospital**. Many of these were built in Victorian times and serve large areas. For this reason they may be quite a long way from your home and difficult to get to. This is particularly so for the hospitals serving big cities like London, as it was thought mental patients needed country air. With the expansion of the cities, this often means they now lie in the outer suburbs of the built-up area.

Finally, if it eventually turns out that someone needs more or less permanent care in hospital, they will be taken into a **long stay ward**. These are almost invariably in the large mental hospitals. Although attempts have been made to 'upgrade' these wards and the décor may be modern and cheerful, it is pretty clear from their limited treatment facilities that they do not get a large share of the available public money. It has been government policy to run down the number of beds in long stay wards and encourage 'community care'. This policy, however, has not been well funded. Alternative care in the community is often very limited; it is really assumed that relatives will provide it, as many of you must know. The policy is likely to continue, however, and in the future there will be far fewer hospital beds for those with long-term problems in mental health.

In psychiatric wards, unlike most medical wards, patients have their own clothes and night clothes, so if your relative is being admitted, she will need to take these with her or you will have to bring them along later. She will be received into the ward by the nursing staff who will register her by taking some personal details. Usually after she has settled in the ward, perhaps an hour or two later, she will be visited by a junior psychiatrist who will make a physical examination, record your relative's mental condition, and set in motion some basic physical investigations. He may provide temporary medication for calming your relative down or to help her sleep. In some hospitals each patient has a key worker, most often a nurse, who has special responsibility for them and co-ordinates all aspects of their care.

Most wards these days are for both sexes. Sleeping accommodation is usually in dormitories with from three to twenty other patients. Each person has his or her own locker by the bed. Some wards do provide single rooms. Most hospitals have one ward which is kept locked, but this is reserved for the most difficult patients, for instance those who are felt likely to commit suicide. A few hospitals have special mother-and-baby units for those with postnatal psychosis. This permits a mentally ill mother to take some part in caring for her baby at this important time.

After a few days, your relative's case will be considered in a **ward round**. The consultant usually presides over this, and there are often quite a number of people there, representing the various clinical professions. This can be upsetting for your relative, and may be equally embarrassing for you if you have been invited along. However, the staff in these meeting are bound by rules of confidentiality, and are there to provide a service for you and your relative. Sometimes, if your relative is likely to be very upset by being seen in the ward round, a few members of the team may come out of the meeting to see her more privately.

Most patients admitted from their homes to psychiatric wards will return home when they are discharged. Usually discharge is planned to take place in a gradual manner: it will be suggested at first that your relative returns home perhaps for an afternoon. Later she may spend, say, Saturday night at home, and if this seems to go all right, perhaps a whole weekend. Eventually she may be discharged provisionally for a few days, 'on leave', before her final official discharge. This pattern can be varied to suit the needs of individual patients and their relatives. During this process it is important that you keep the clinical staff informed about how things have gone, and what you think the next step should be.

Sometimes, other accommodation may seem a better option. There are a number of possibilities, including **supervised hostels**, **group homes** and **supervised lodgings**.

Hostels, which may be established either by the statutory authorities or by charitable organisations, provide for a number of patients. They vary enormously: some are just places to eat and sleep, others have much more in the way of supervision. Some provide long-term accommodation, whereas others are seen very much as staging posts in a full return to life in the community. In some, supervision is quite intensive, with night staff and organised daytime activities. The aim is to place people in the facility that best suits their level of disability, although this may not always be possible.

Group homes are usually set up in large converted houses. There may be from four to twenty patients living in them. After the settling-in period, they are not heavily supervised, although various members of the psychiatric team may pop in from time to time. In most ways they are just like an ordinary home. The residents have their own rooms, but will share other facilities. They have to work out amongst themselves who does what in the important matters of cooking and cleaning. Some will go out to work or to day centres during the day. In some homes, there is a limit to the length of time someone can live there. Obviously, you and your ill relative must know about this.

Some people provide accommodation by letting spare rooms in their houses to people recovering from mental illness. They may also provide cooked meals. Arrangements for visits from social workers or CPNs usually have to be made separately, as does attendance at day care facilities. Sometimes the landlord may insist that lodgers are out of the house during the day. Some local authorities have lists of people who are willing to take in mentally ill lodgers and have been good at looking after them in the past.

Local authorities do have a responsibility to provide accommodation for people leaving psychiatric hospitals if it is needed, provided they previously lived within their boundaries. This accommodation may be in another area, although the first authority will **sponsor** people to live in it through a financial arrangement with the second authority. This system has been abused recently by local authorities in large cities sponsoring discharged mental patients to live in seaside resorts where they have no kind of community support. Some local authorities and voluntary organisations will provide sheltered flats and bed-sitters. The accommodation may be purpose-built, or a number of flats in a block may be given over to people recovering from mental illnesses. Some support is given, sometimes by social workers or housing officers, sometimes by volunteer helpers. This may be an ideal arrangement for some mentally ill people.

A variety of charitable organisations are involved in the creation of accommodation for former hospital patients. These include the Richmond Fellowship, the Mental After-Care Association, the Psychiatric Rehabilitation Association and several local branches of MIND.

The decision for a patient to move from home into one of these facilities should be a joint one by the patient, the relatives they live with, and the clinical team.

People who have longstanding psychiatric problems may

require particular services to **rehabilitate** them. This means helping them to get started again after having been mentally ill. It may include relearning old skills, such as working to a routine, or acquiring new skills, as required for some particular job, or new interests such as painting or pottery. It may also mean helping a sufferer to regain the confidence needed to go back out into the community. It is usually a very gradual process, certainly not one that can be hurried, so that staff may see it in terms of months or years, particularly for someone who has had several bouts of illness.

Many rehabilitation services provide a working environment. They include facilities that are especially designed to help mentally ill people, but some are more general and available to other members of the public. As might be expected, some of the facilities are closely connected with psychiatric wards and hospitals. The occupational therapy unit deals with a wide range of the skills needed for everyday living. Industrial therapy units are more specifically geared to providing a working environment, however gently the patient is introduced to it. Some hospitals incorporate a **day hospital**. Patients come to this during the day from their homes and the emphasis is very much on rehabilitation. Occasionally, the day hospital may be seen as an alternative to full-time admission, but usually it is used by recently discharged patients. It will often have its own occupational therapy and industrial therapy unit. The principles of occupational and industrial therapy are described in more detail below. It may be a good idea for you to ask about the social facilities the hospital provides for patients and to enquire whether any of these would be suitable for your sick relative. The best person to ask is probably the team's social worker.

There are also **day centres**. These are supposed to be provided by local authorities. No local authority, however, has so far set up the number of day centres required by government guidelines, and some have set up none at all. The activities in day centres are not very different from those in day hospitals, but the level of supervision is less. It is possible to obtain information about the range of local authority provision for the mentally ill from your local social services department.

When we first started to work in psychiatry, a normal aim of treatment and rehabilitation was for our patients to return to full-time employment. Even now, people who suffer from the more minor psychiatric disorders assume that they will go back to their job when they are better. However, times have certainly changed for those who become more seriously ill, particularly with a disorder like schizophrenia which often impairs performance even when the more acute symptoms have abated. Even in the South-East, many of these people either never return to outside employment, or have infrequent temporary jobs.

Nevertheless, there are facilities which are geared towards helping mental patients return to employment, and which recognise that this may be a long process. Some are run by statutory authorities, some by voluntary agencies. Attendance may involve getting back into a previous work routine, for instance factory or clerical work, or retraining for some new occupation.

The facilities that may sometimes find a place in rehabilitating particular individuals recovering from mental illness include local authority rehabilitation and assessment centres, community-based industrial units, sheltered industrial groups, employment rehabilitation centres, skill centres, residential training colleges, and colleges of further education.

Organisations that provide employment include Remploy, the Psychiatric Rehabilitation Association, the Richmond Fellowship, and some local branches of MIND. As well as training and rehabilitation, these organisations provide guidance about many aspects of the return to open employment. However, it may be that your relative never makes the transfer to a job in the outside world. Sheltered employment may then become a reasonable and rewarding option.

Many people who have recovered from a mental illness

and are returning to the hurly-burly of the employment market will initially need additional help. This can be obtained from the Disablement Resettlement Officer (DRO) who works in your local Job Centre. In this country any firm that employs more than 20 people must reserve three per cent of its posts for persons who are registered as disabled. This may help your relative in getting a job — it is the DRO's responsibility to consider placing someone on the Disabled Person's Register. However, there is still often a long waiting list.

Sometimes it may be possible for your relative to get practical guidance on the frequently harrowing business of attending job interviews. This may be provided by professionals from the organisation that is helping to get him or her back into employment, but can also be obtained from the psychologist or occupational therapist on the psychiatric team.

People who become mentally ill may lose their job. However, mental illness on its own is not grounds for dismissal. If your relative's employers wanted to dismiss him, they would need to ask your relative to provide a medical report concerning his fitness to work. If the doctor providing the report was of the opinion that your relative would not be able to work again for a year, the employers would then be in a position to dismiss him. They could also dismiss him for poor performance at work if this was apparent. However, the employers cannot dismiss someone for either of these reasons without giving warning and, if they do so, your relative has in any case the right to appeal to an industrial tribunal within three months. MIND's legal advice department (at head office) can advise them or you about the legal position over dismissal on grounds of mental illness.

Dealing with mental health professionals

If you live with someone who has had a severe mental illness, it almost inevitably means that you will come into close and

perhaps frequent contact with mental health staff. Unfortunately, these relationships are often uncomfortable for both
sides. This may sometimes make obtaining treatment or help
for your sick relative or for yourself more difficult than it
need be, and may even impair the sufferer's progress. It is
extremely important that you should try not to be intimidated in your interviews with staff. Do not be dissuaded
from asking any questions you want to, or from expressing
concern over what worries you.

Often, these staff-relative relationships start badly because
of an upsetting hospital admission that relatives, patients or
even staff may afterwards feel has not been handled properly.
If your first introduction to the local mental health facilities
involves following your relative screaming down a long
corridor late at night, accompanied by police and other
people in uniform, this may make subsequent relationships
difficult. Such scenes are rare, but if someone has developed
a serious mental illness and is unwilling to be seen by a
psychiatrist, or refuses to go to hospital, the result may be
a crisis that is very unpleasant and shocking for all concerned.
Sometimes, such crises happen very suddenly and are quite
unavoidable, but it is natural to want to blame someone,
and clinical staff may be a convenient, and sometimes
justified, target.

After your relative has been admitted, staff will usually
want to ask you many questions about his or her early
history, the existence of any problems in the past and inti-
mate details of his relationships, and sometimes, if it is
relevant, of yours, too. The clinical staff see it as necessary
to obtain the maximum amount of information about a
patient as quickly as possible after an admission, and a relative is normally the best person to provide this. However,
relatives often feel that these questions are unnecessarily
intrusive and endlessly repeated. They may also think the
situation is unfairly one-sided, as their own questions and
queries are not answered. To an extent, this situation arises
because of the unhurried way the psychiatric team uses infor-

mation and observation to come to firm and safe conclusions. However, a few professionals also have particular difficulties in talking openly with relatives. This, of course, is crazy — if a psychiatrist cannot feel easy in talking to people, who can? — but, as we say, it is still sometimes the case. Some professionals have particular difficulties in admitting that they do not know the answer to a given question, although relatives have a right to know this.

The staff's assessment of a patient, of what treatment will be best, and of how someone will respond to it, usually takes some weeks to complete, and may indeed continue to change as more information becomes available. This delay can be frustrating for you as a relative: the psychiatric team will often hesitate for weeks or even months after admission or initial assessment before deciding on the best treatments for someone. Even then, they may still be hesitant or even evasive about telling you of these decisions. Moreover, it may never have been made clear who within the team is responsible for saying what to whom. It may be therefore quite hard for you to get from staff any authoritative statement about what is wrong with your relative. Instant answers to insistent questions are unlikely to be available. Staff may not know the answers, or may be reluctant to tell relatives and risk upsetting them by being too pessimistic. Unfortunately, it is impossible to be sure about the likely course of a severe episode of mental illness, and this may account for most of the reticence that relatives encounter. While we know that some patients will recover completely, it may not be possible at the outset to recognise them, so staff may not be able to impart precise information. However, more general information should be available.

Clearly, however, if you feel you are not getting the information you need, you must make this plain to the staff. It is reasonable for you to ask to speak to the consultant psychiatrist or other members of the clinical team to discuss their views on your relative's problems, the sorts of treatments available, what can be expected on their return home, and the staff member's opinion on the sort of mental illness it is and how your relative is recovering from it.

The team's **Social Workers** may be particularly useful to you here, as they often have a special interest in the family as a whole. Their viewpoint can be a major and helpful addition to information obtained from other members of staff. The way to contact social workers differs from hospital to hospital. Sometimes a 'referral' has to be made by the psychiatrist, in other places it is more informal. Most psychiatric hospitals have a Social Work Department which will tell you how to get in contact. Otherwise the nursing staff may be able to advise you.

It is often useful to have more than one appointment with staff, as it may be impossible for you to ask all your questions and remember the answers during an initial interview. Do not be afraid to take a notebook to record what you are being told, or to ask for explanations if difficult technical terms are used. You should not hide the fact of your visit from your ill relative (it is, after all, perfectly reasonable for you to want to find out as much as possible about his or her illness), but how much you discuss what was said will depend on the exact circumstances.

Not all the problems of getting information are due to the uncertainty of the situation or the inadequacies of the staff. It is possible to be told something and not really take it on board, especially if the experience is novel and you are distressed by it. It usually takes time, much more time than with a more straightforward physical illness, for relatives to take in exactly what is happening to the patient. It may be many months before you come to an understanding of some of the causes (which even the staff may be unsure of) and are able to accept some of the long-term implications of a severe mental illness for your relative and for the family as a whole.

You are likely to experience a range of emotions at this difficult time. You may feel that staff do not consult you over treatment decisions, or give you adequate support, and even that they are blaming you for your relative's problems. You may well feel very confused and worried about the future. It is usually a great relief that someone else is now coping with your relative for a while, but such feelings may also make you feel very guilty. Other feelings that people in your position have described include those of inadequacy, hopelessness, bitterness that these things have happened at all and great upset that the patient has become so ill. It is not surprising that the attempts of staff and relatives to communicate with each other are often unsuccessful.

Many find that **self-help groups**, formed together with other relatives, provide a useful place where they can obtain information and exchange experiences. One such organisation is the National Schizophrenia Fellowship, which is described in some detail on pp. 134–5. Talking to relatives who have been through it all before can be a great help to you if you are going through a bad patch. You in turn may be able to help others at a later date. Professional people can be invited to speak to such a group from time to time and to answer questions.

Second opinions
In the National Health Service, it is accepted that patients will sometimes want an opinion from another doctor. If your relative wants such a **second opinion**, she must find a doctor willing to examine her, and there is no obligation on any given doctor to do this. In general, the doctor in charge of her case will be agreeable to her seeking a second opinion and there will be no difficulty in doing so. Your relative may do this entirely through your family doctor, but if she herself discovers a psychiatrist willing to see her, the family doctor will probably agree to make a formal referral for her.

There may occasionally be particular problems for psychiatric patients who want to be referred for the opinion of another doctor. Psychiatric hospitals are responsible for all the people living in a particular area, and these **catchment**

areas are rigidly observed. It may therefore be difficult to obtain the opinion of a doctor working in a hospital which deals with another area. The doctors attached to a given hospital are likely to work closely together and your relative may feel, with some justification, that a second opinion from a close colleague of her own doctor might be prejudiced. The psychiatrist may also be tempted to feel that her reluctance to accept a first opinion is due to her psychiatric state.

The situation for the mentally ill is therefore sometimes unsatisfactory. One way round the problem is to seek a second opinion from a psychiatrist in a hospital with a medical school (a **Teaching Hospital**). There are many of these in London, and most large cities have one. The services that teaching hospitals provide are not usually restricted to their catchment area. The disadvantage of this method of obtaining a second opinion is that it may involve travelling quite a distance. Your family doctor can make the referral, although it is useful if you or your relative can supply the name of a doctor you would like to consult at the hospital. However, the Royal College of Psychiatrists makes it a rule *not* to give out the names of suitable psychiatrists, so you would have to ferret around a bit to find a name for yourself.

It is possible to seek a further opinion **privately**, that is, outside the National Health Service. There will be a fee for this opinion. Your doctor may know a psychiatrist who sees patients in this way. Any long-term private medical treatment is very expensive indeed, particularly if it involves frequent hospital in-patient treatment, but you may feel that an appointment for a second opinion is worth paying for if it sets your mind at rest. Private medical insurance schemes may not cover psychiatric care.

Detained patients have the right to a second opinion under the Mental Health Act: the Mental Health Act Commission has the duty of appointing a doctor to provide this second opinion.

We have given advice on how you can best set about obtaining what you need for your relative and yourself from the psychiatric services. There are, however, still places in this country where local facilities are underfunded or under-developed, or the local professionals are apathetic, ignorant or unsympathetic. Sometimes, through great efforts, you may be able to browbeat them into extending the provision they offer to you and your relative. In some circumstances, no adequate service is forthcoming, try as you might, and you may have to turn more towards independent organis-ations, such as the **National Schizophrenia Fellowship**, the **Manic Depression Fellowship** or **MIND**. Such organ-isations offer information and support, but they may also be able to exert pressure on the authorities to develop local facilities.

4 Treatment

There are several treatments that are offered routinely for severe mental illness in NHS hospitals in all parts of the country. These may include **admission** to hospital, **physical treatments** like electroconvulsive therapy (ECT) and drug therapy, and various **social treatments**. They are all described below. Private medical care tends to offer a similar approach.

ADMISSION TO HOSPITAL

If your relative has just become ill with severe depression, mania or schizophrenia, he is most likely to be offered **hospital admission**. Though this does not at first sight seem to be a form of treatment, removing someone from a situation where he has been overwhelmed by worries and stresses may well cause his symptoms to improve. Rest, routine and nursing care all add to the beneficial effects of being in hospital. At its best, a mental ward provides a relatively neutral environment where someone's exact symptoms and behaviour can be assessed, usually over a period of several weeks.

You and your relative may, however, find such an admission very upsetting, especially if it is the first time he has been admitted and the ward is noisy. Not infrequently, however, the patient finds this less upsetting than his family. When someone has been advised that he should be admitted to hospital but refuses, the psychiatrist may, on rare occasions, decide that it is in the patient's interest to be admitted 'under a section', that is, without his consent through the powers of the Mental Health Act (see pp. 139–40). While relatives usually see the necessity of compulsory admission, they may be understandably distressed. Some may be left feeling very guilty, as if they have 'betrayed' the patient.

In addition, you yourself may never have visited a mental hospital before. Mental hospitals, and mental illness itself, are still seen as frightening or shameful by many people. There is often an image, unfortunately confirmed by the more lurid films and TV programmes, that once you enter a mental hospital you do not return, and that people who live there are bizarre and terrifying. The reality is more commonplace, and mental hospitals have, in any case, changed considerably, especially since the 1950s. Nevertheless, some old mental hospitals retain a forbidding exterior or an isolated position, which can take some time to get used to. Some newer psychiatric facilities are based in District General Hospitals, and this may make an admission easier to accept and more convenient. When it is not the first time a patient has been admitted, both relative and patient will know more of what they have to deal with.

You may find it hard to visit your relative in hospital, perhaps because of practical inconvenience, perhaps because you do not really relish the ward environment. Nevertheless, your relative will very probably set great store by your visits, so try to go as often as possible. Apart from the requirements of ward activities like OT (see p. 128), visiting is usually fairly unrestricted. When you visit, it will normally be all right to go for a walk or out to a local café with your relative, although you should tell the nursing staff what you are doing.

'PHYSICAL' TREATMENT

Drugs in mental illness

Effective treatments in psychiatry are of really quite recent date. Before the 1950s, psychiatrists had little to offer their patients except sedation and nursing care. If people got better, it was usually the result of the natural ebb and flow of their illness. However, around that time there were a number of innovations, which included ECT, the first drugs effective against schizophrenia and depression, and the development of techniques of rehabilitation. Older clinicians who can remember those times will say how dramatic the effect of introducing these new treatments really was. It became possible to empty whole wards.

Nowadays, the rate of improvement is much slower. All the new drugs that have come out recently are really variations on themes established in the 1950s. Usually they are improvements not because they are any more effective in making people better, but because they have less in the way of side effects. However, when we carp at the use and possible overuse of medication in psychiatry, it is worth remembering that dramatic beginning.

New drug treatments in psychiatry arise because a pharmaceutical company develops a new preparation. This must be subjected to very careful testing to establish its effectiveness and its freedom from side effects before it is granted a licence and can be prescribed in the normal way.

Most people will be offered some sort of drug treatment during their hospital admission. Although drugs are never the complete answer to a mental illness, they are often a necessary first step, providing a platform on which other types of treatment can build. In the treatment of psychiatric conditions, drugs are often continued after a person returns home, sometimes for many months or years. Many people have expressed worries that psychiatrists use drugs merely in order to keep patients quiet, and that large doses are prescribed without proper consideration of their possible bad effects. There are some grounds for this worry, but most psychiatrists these days weigh the benefits and disadvantages of treatment carefully. Nevertheless, if you feel that you see changes in your relatives that might be due to the unwanted effects of medication, it is reasonable to share your worry with the psychiatrist in charge of treatment. However, such changes can be the result, not of the drugs, but of the underlying illness, so it is difficult to be sure of their cause. This section will describe the **sorts of effects** that may arise from taking the drugs that psychiatrists commonly use.

One of the problems with drugs in this country is that they all have at least two names. This can be confusing. First is the approved or 'generic' name of the compound — examples include diazepam or amitriptyline. Then the pharmaceutical companies give their product their own name, which is different – so diazepam may become Valium, and amitriptyline Tryptizol. The company name is distinguished from the generic name by having a capital initial letter. If, as sometimes happens, several companies each have their own brand of a drug, the picture becomes very complicated indeed. Doctors are encouraged to use the generic names, but often they do not. In this book, we are quite inconsistent about it, going really for the name you are most likely to have come across.

There are several different sorts of medication that may be prescribed for the severe mental illnesses we are concerned with here. Some are given in tablet or capsule form, others are **long-acting**, and can be given by injection weekly or less frequently. Many people end up preferring this long-acting medication, as it has to be taken less often and they do not have to worry about remembering when their tablets are due. It does mean that some of the control of medication is taken from the patient, as the drug remains in the body for a few weeks after the last injection. Some patients find this unacceptable.

The medicine given to patients will vary according to the type of illness they have. Schizophrenia is usually treated with **major tranquillisers**. Examples you may have heard of include Largactil, Serenace or Modecate, but there are now many of these drugs available. We list these in Table 1 and Table 2. Acute attacks of mania are also usually treated with medicines from this group.

TABLE 1
Major Tranquillisers

NAME	PROPRIETARY NAME	MORE COMMON SIDE EFFECTS
Clopenthixol	Clopixol	restlessness
Chlorpromazine	Largactil	tremor
Chlorprothixene	Taractan	stiffness
Droperidol	Droleptan	loss of facial
Flupenthixol	Depixol	expression
Fluphenazine	Moditen	dry mouth
Haloperidol	Haldol	blurred vision
	Serenace	constipation
Oxypertine	Integrin	difficulty in passing
Pericyazine	Neulactil	water
Perphenazine	Fentazin	increased appetite
Pimozide	Orap	faintness on suddenly
Prochloroperazine	Stemetil	standing up
	Vertigon	sensitivity of skin
	spansules	to sunlight
Promazine	Sparine	lowering of body
Sulpiridine	Dolmatil	temperature
Thiopropazate	Dartalan	odd movements of the
Thioridazine	Melleril	body and face
Trifluoroperazine	Stelazine	increases the effect
Trifluperidol	Triperidol	of alcohol

Not every drug shows all of these effects to the same extent. Side effects are often temporary.

TABLE 2

Major Tranquillisers Given by Injection
*(side effects are similar to those
when medication is given by mouth)*

NAME	PROPRIETARY NAME
Clopenthixol decanoate	Clopixol
Flupenthixol decanoate	Depixol
Fluphenazine decanoate	Modecate
Fluphenazine enanthate	Moditen
Fluspirilene	Redeptin
Haloperodol decanoate	Haldol decanoate
Pipothiazine palmitate	Piportil depot

The major tranquillisers are so called because of their effects on severe psychiatric disturbance. The **minor tranquillisers**, such as Valium, work in a different way and are used for different conditions. The major tranquillisers do tranquillise, that is, they do calm the patient down, but their particular effect is to reduce the more disturbing symptoms, such as hallucinations, odd ideas or difficulties in thinking. In most people this means the more severe problems of the illness can be controlled, but it may not mean they disappear completely, or that the drugs are effective all the time. While the major tranquillisers are often very effective in treating the more dramatic features of the illness, they have little effect on negative symptoms. Unlike the minor group, the major tranquillisers do not seem to be addictive.

It is also true the drugs do not necessarily make a schizophrenic or manic patient feel 'better'. During a straightforward physical illness like an infection, it is usually quickly obvious that medication reduces fever and improves well-being. In contrast, drugs used for these severe mental illnesses may have no effects discernible to the patient, who may even feel worse for a time. This is because it may take some days or weeks before the benefits of major tranquillisers become apparent, as adequate levels of the drug in the body are reached only gradually. However, for those who do not agree that there is anything wrong with them, being given drugs that seem unnecessary can be very disturbing.

You yourself may also find this issue very difficult, if you, too, are unable to see immediate benefits of drug treatment. Often, however, relatives can see quite clearly that the patient's refusal to take the drugs has a bad effect on the course of the illness. Their help in encouraging patients to take their drugs can be crucial.

The medication can then work to help the patient become gradually more in touch with reality and easier to talk to.

Most medicines have several effects: the unwanted ones are called **side effects**. Those of the major tranquillisers may include dry mouth, and weight gain (see Tables 1 and 2). In addition, they can produce symptoms rather like those of Parkinson's disease — slowing, restlessness, trembling and muscle stiffness. This is called 'drug-induced Parkinsonism'. However these side effects usually pass off in a few weeks, and other tablets can be taken to reduce them.

There has been much concern recently over the issue of 'tardive diskinesia'. This is a movement disorder which comes on after many months' or years' treatment with major tranquillisers. The most prominent and frequent effect is a continual grimacing, which the poor sufferer usually seems unaware of. So far no effective treatment of this condition has been discovered, and it does not normally get better. However, it is not entirely clear that it is a drug side effect. Such grimacings were described in schizophrenia long before major tranquillisers, and are still sometimes reported in sufferers who have not yet been prescribed these drugs.

For most patients an optimum balance can be achieved between the untoward effects and the beneficial 'calming down' effects of the tranquillising drugs. However, patients who are not convinced of the benefits can become very concerned with the side effects, and may refuse to take any medication at all. Unfortunately, this sometimes means the initial illness returns. In the same way that they take some

time to build up a **therapeutic effect**, the drugs often take
some days or weeks to wear off. This means there may be
no immediate change when patients stop taking them, so
they may feel their decision was justified.

David was a man of 22 who was admitted to hospital
because he was acutely disturbed. He had been rushing out
of his house, shouting at passers-by and telling them to leave
him alone. He thought they were spying on him and that
there was an evil and complicated plot afoot to harm him.
He continued to be upset in hospital and he was given
Largactil, at first in moderate doses, but when this did not
have any effect, in quite large doses. Over a period of a few
days he settled down and was less frightened. Gradually he
lost his delusional ideas and was able to take part in the ward
activities. He did become quite shaky for about ten days,
almost certainly as a result of the Largactil. However, this
wore off without the need either for reducing the dose or
for giving further medication to neutralise it. After about
eight weeks he was discharged, but it was felt that he should
continue to take medication, although in much lower doses.
In fact he still takes it, and it seems to have been effective in
preventing the return of his frightening persecutory ideas.
He did discontinue it for a few weeks, but was strongly
advised to start it again when he had a minor return of his
old suspiciousness.

David's experience with medication was a happy one, and
he has no objection to continuing with it. He does not like
to talk about the ideas he had, and gives the impression this
is because he thinks they show him in rather a foolish light.
It appears, though, that he thinks of medication as a small
price to pay to prevent their return.

Clearly, not all sufferers are equally happy with medication. In some this will be because they think they never
needed it or at any rate no longer need it, in others because
they have side effects they do not like. In some very severe
cases of schizophrenia, the psychiatrist may prescribe medication with the hope of only marginal benefit, trading off

unpleasant side effects against the anguish that could be caused to the sufferer by letting the disease get out of control. This can be a very fine judgement, and there is no doubt that psychiatrists sometimes get it wrong: they have a tendency to err on the cautious side, although these days they are becoming more wary of the dangers of doing harm with the major tranquillisers. Under these circumstances of having to weight the balance of advantage so carefully, it is not impossible for you to see things differently from your relative's psychiatrist. This may be because either you or they do not have all the information against which the correct prescription of medication must be judged. If you feel strongly about this, talking to your relative's psychiatrist will at least clear the air, and may lead to a modification of treatment.

It is in fact possible for some people with schizophrenia even of a fairly enduring type to manage without medication, although this may be at the cost of a more restricted life style, by which they avoid overstimulation. Provided they are not actually a danger to themselves or to others, this is a choice they have a right to make, although it may sometimes make things harder for those who look after them, whether relatives or clinicians.

Depression can be treated with **antidepressants**. There are two main groups of these. The most commonly used group, the **tricyclic antidepressants**, includes drugs like Tofranil, Tryptizol, Prothiaden and Bolvidon (see Table 3). Again, there are many for the doctor to choose from. Another group, the **monoamine oxidase inhibitors** (MAOIs), includes Nardil and Parnate but is used less often (Table 4).

Antidepressants are quite effective in restoring the **chemical imbalance** thought to underlie moderate and severe depression. It takes a few days before mood begins to lift, so the tablets have to be taken exactly as prescribed. It is likely to be several weeks, and in some cases even longer, before mood is completely normal, and the psychiatrist will

TABLE 3
Cyclic Antidepressants

NAME	PROPRIETARY NAME	COMMON SIDE EFFECTS
Amitriptyline	Tryptizol	
	Domical	
	Elavil	
	Lentizol (S-R)	
	Saroten	
Butriptyline	Evadyne	
Clomipramine	Anafranil	Dry mouth
Desipramine	Pertofran	Blurred vision
Dibenzepin	Noveril	Constipation
Dothiepin	Prothiaden	Difficulty in
Doxepin	Sinequan	passing water
Imipramine	Tofranil	Weight gain
	Berkomine	Confusion in the
	Praminil	elderly
Iprindole	Prondol	Occasional worsening
Lofepramine	Gamanil	of symptoms
Maprotiline	Ludiomil	in those with
Mianserin	Bolvidon	schizophrenia
	Norval	Increase in the effect
Nomifensine	Merital	of alcohol
Nortriptyline	Allegron	
	Aventyl	
Protriptyline	Concordin	
Trazodone	Molipaxin	
Trimipramine	Surmontil	
Viloxazine	Vivalan	
Fluvoxamine	Faverin	

Side effects tend to wear off over a few days and are less prominent if the dose is gradually increased to full levels.

TABLE 4
MAOI Antidepressants

DRUG	PROPRIETARY NAME	COMMON SIDE EFFECTS
Iproniazid	Marsilid	faintness on suddenly standing up
Isocarboxazid	Marplan	
Phenelzine	Nardil	
Tranylcypromine	Parnate	dangerous interactions with some other drug
		dangerous interactions with some foods (cheese, etc.)
		increase in the effect of alcohol

Because of their interactions with other substances, these drugs are less commonly prescribed nowadays. All patients receiving these should carry a treatment card which gives details of the interactions.

probably continue to prescribe this medication for some time after that.

Antidepressants do have some immediate effects. Some make patients feel drowsy, others may have an energising effect. This may interfere with the patient's ability to drive. Complaints of a dry mouth or of blurred vision are not uncommon, but these side effects usually become less noticeable over a few days. The effects of **alcohol** are increased in people taking these drugs. The MAOI group of antidepressants interact with certain foodstuffs that contain high levels of **tyramine**, particularly cheese. These reactions can be dangerous: there is a rapid rise in blood pressure with severe headache. Very occasionally, the reaction can trigger off a stroke. Patients prescribed this type of drug are given **cards** by the pharmacy listing all the foods to be avoided. This list is given in Table 5.

TABLE 5

Foods to be avoided by those taking
Monoamine Oxidase Inhibitors

Cheese (especially cream cheese)
Meat and yeast extracts (e.g. Bovril, Marmite, Oxo)
Broad Beans
Avocado pears
Pickled herrings
Food which might be 'going off' (especially meat, fish, poultry)
Proprietary cough and cold medicines (i.e. bought over the
    counter at a pharmacists)
Chocolate, yoghurt, cream and game may also produce reaction,
    although more rarely

The effect of alcohol is increased by these drugs, but in addition red wine can set off the same reaction as the foods above.

You will remember Sue, the depressed teacher we spoke of in Chapter 1. You might like to know what happened to her. She was suffering from the sort of depression that a psychiatrist would immediately recognise as likely to benefit from a tricyclic antidepressant. She was prescribed Prothiaden, although she would probably have responded equally to a number of others from this group. At first she was given a small dose, but over a few days this was increased to a moderately large one. This gradual introduction of the drug was deliberate, as it lessens the chance of side effects. She did notice her mouth was dry and she felt a little bit woozy. In fact, as she was feeling pretty rotten anyway, the wooziness did not matter and, if anything, took the edge off her anguish. At first, there was little change, but after a

fortnight or so she was able to report a slight lightening in
the gloom. Over the following few weeks she gradually
improved, and after two months was able to return to work.
She had started enjoying herself again. Her husband was
delighted to have back the wife he had known. She was once
more a sociable, loving and energetic woman. Apart from
the antidepressant, little treatment was required beyond
support through the bad period, and some advice about
the general management of her life. The medication was
continued for about three months after she had fully
recovered — just occasionally, someone who appears
completely better may relapse if antidepressants are stopped
too quickly.

Patients who have repeated episodes of depression, and
especially those who also have experienced an episode of
mania, may be prescribed **lithium**. Whilst this does have an
effect on acute symptoms, its main use is to make relapse
less likely. It may take a year, or even more, before it can
be seen to be effective, and it therefore involves patients
taking medication whilst free of symptoms. From time to
time the psychiatrist will want a **blood test** to determine
the level of this drug in the body. This is to ensure the
correct dose and an absence of side effects, as the correct dose
lies in a fairly narrow band between one that is ineffective and
one that produces unwanted effects. Monitoring ensures that
only a tiny minority of patients suffer significant side effects.
Nevertheless, it can sometimes happen that the level becomes
too high. Symptoms that suggest this possibility are listed
in Table 6.

Jeremy, a quiet scholarly man who worked in a bank, had
experienced three rather damaging breakdowns. The first
looked like schizophrenia, but by the time of the third it
became clear that the likely diagnosis was manic depressive
illness. His employers had been tolerant of his illness, despite
the fact that his behaviour when ill had brought adverse
publicity to them. However, their tolerance could not be
boundless. It was decided to start treatment with lithium,

and Jeremy has now taken it for ten years without any recurrence of illness. His only complaint is that he finds it hard to lose weight.

TABLE 6
Side Effects of Lithium

Early and fleeting	Nausea Diarrhoea Metallic taste }	Action: mention to doctor. Not dangerous
Persistent	Weight gain	
	Shakiness Increased consumption of water Increased amounts of urine }	Mention to doctor as a matter of urgency. It may be necessary to reduce the number of tablets.

Gillian also did well on lithium. However, she developed considerable swelling of the ankles, and it was decided to take her off the medication. While this was sensible in terms of her physical condition, it did mean she had a return of symptoms from time to time that led to her admission to hospital on two occasions and caused considerable strain for her family.

Recently, it has been found that the drug **carbamezepine** can be used successfully to prevent the return of manic depressive symptoms, sometimes in people for whom other treatments have failed. Gillian was started on carbamezepine and has been very well ever since.

Sometimes, if a person suffers from depressive delusions, the psychiatrist will prescribe major tranquillisers like those used in schizophrenia. These can be quite effective in this condition, too. Occasionally, people with these illnesses may be given **minor tranquillisers**, such as Valium or Librium (see Table 7). These do not help to cure an attack directly,

TABLE 7
Minor Tranquillisers

NAME	PROPRIETARY NAMES	COMMON SIDE EFFECTS
Triazolam	Halcion	
Alprazolam	Xanax	
Bromazepam	Lexotan	
Flunitrazepam	Rohypnol	
Lorazepam	Almazine	
	Ativan	
Lormetazepam	Noctamid	
Oxazepam	Serenid-D	
Temazepam	Euhypnos	
	Normison	
Chlordiazepoxide	Librium	Drowsiness
Clobazepam	Frisium	Confusion
Clorazepate	Tranxene	Impaired performance
Diazepam	Alupram	on physical tasks
	Atensine	like driving,
	Diazemuls	working machinery
	Evacalm	Increase in the effect
	Solis	of alcohol
	Stesolid	Addiction
	Valium Roche	
	Valrelease	
Flurazepam	Dalmane	
Ketazolam	Anxon	
Medazepam	Nobrium	
Nitrazepam	Mogadon	
	Nitrados	
	Sommite	
	Surem	
	Unisomnia	
Parazepam	Centrax	

The compounds in italics above are those which can be prescribed under the National Health Service for the treatment of anxiety. NHS prescriptions cannot be made for specific proprietary preparations. Patients must now pay for a private prescription for these and for the drugs which are not italicised.

but may calm someone who is particularly agitated. Psychiatrists are increasingly reluctant to prescribe these drugs and will do so only in certain restricted circumstances, as they are now known to be **addictive**. When they are prescribed, the psychiatrist will these days aim to discontinue them as soon as possible, certainly within a few months. In some cases, when people have been taking minor tranquillisers for years, it may be impracticable to discontinue them, especially if other problems seem more important. People aiming to come off the drugs after a long period should do so under medical supervision as there may be **withdrawal effects**, especially if it is done too quickly. A list of the withdrawal effects is given in Table 8. Some of this group cannot now be prescribed under the NHS (see Table 7).

It is difficult for all concerned if someone refuses to take prescribed medication. It may not be possible to convince a

TABLE 8
Withdrawal symptoms of minor tranquillisers

---

apprehension and anxiety
loss of appetite
faintness, lightheadedness or unsteadiness
fatigue
sleep disturbance
shakiness, muscle twitches, muscle cramps in legs
pins and needles
hypersensitivity to sensation
vomiting

These symptoms are likely to come on a few days after stopping the medication, and usually do so only after someone has been taking appreciable doses for six months or so. In some instances, the symptoms may appear like 'flu or gastroenteritis. They can also resemble an anxiety state, except for the muscle twitches. Not everyone is equally liable to withdrawal symptoms.

reluctant patient that medication is helpful until it has had some effect, and they are sufficiently in touch with reality again to feel these effects. People with manic depressive illness may refuse to take lithium because they actually miss feeling 'high'. Hopefully, with support from relatives, a sympathetic doctor will be able to work out the best and most acceptable drug dosage. This can often be gradually reduced as the patient improves.

Some patients are **not** helped despite very large doses of medication, and yet others need to continue to take it for long periods of time without any obvious benefit, but in order to prevent a recurrence of illness. In the early stages it is usually not possible to tell how a given person will respond to drug treatment, or how long they will need to take it. The doctor will keep a close eye on medication, and may vary it from time to time to allow for this.

Occasionally, you or your sick relative may feel the doctor is issuing repeat prescriptions without assessing the need for them properly. This impression may be a true one, but sometimes arises because of a lack of communication. In either case, it is reasonable for you to seek an opportunity to express your concern to the doctor in order to clarify the situation.

Problems over taking medication
It may happen that you suspect that your mentally ill relative might be lying about taking his tablets. In this difficult situation, it is probably not a good idea to confront him immediately. One reasonable course of action is to accompany him to the next appointment with the psychiatrist. Ask to see the psychiatrist separately, and explain the problem. Alternatively, you could do this over the phone. Suggest you might supervise your relative's drug treatment to some extent. To do this, you obviously need to be very clear about the correct dosage, when the medication is to be taken, and the likelihood of any side effects.

You can then tell your relative that the psychiatrist wants you to help with medication. Remind your relative when the tablets are due, and watch as he or she takes them. Having established, to some extent, your right to take an interest in this way, it may then also be possible to raise the question of the tablet you find down the toilet, or of the bottle fuller than it should be. How you handle this obviously depends on your relationship and whether the necessary frankness can be tolerated. It will not be useful if all you manage to change is the method of disposal.

ECT (electroconvulsive therapy)
This treatment is sometimes referred to as 'shock treatment', an unfortunate name that is bound to frighten both patients and relatives. It is therefore important for you to know something about it, should it be offered. ECT has caused considerable controversy, both within the profession of psychiatry and among members of the public. There is no doubt at all that in the past it was used too frequently, and in cases where benefit would have been unlikely. On the other hand, in those days, psychiatrists had little to offer in the way of effective physical treatment, and so may sometimes have used it where there was only the remotest hope that it would work. Nowadays it is prescribed much less frequently. For carefully chosen patients it is the most effective treatment, and in the severest depression or mania it may be life-saving.

It is most commonly used in **manic depressive illness**, particularly **severe depression**, and especially if the sufferer has **delusions**.

Before a patient is given ECT, the treatment is explained and he or she is then asked to sign a **consent form** (which is invalid unless the explanation has been given). Only in special circumstances may ECT be given if the patient refuses or if he is too ill to give proper consent (see p. 147).

The procedure is carefully controlled. The patient lies on

a bed, and is given a special **short-acting anaesthetic** and
a **muscle relaxant**. A small electric current is then passed
through the brain from electrodes applied to the head. The
electric current sets off a sort of epileptic fit. Such fits result
from a simultaneous discharge of the nerve cells of the brain,
and this necessarily involves the release of **transmitter
substances**. This seems to restore the **chemical imbalance**
in the brain thought to be responsible for manic depressive
illness. For improvement to occur, it is necessary that a fit
should take place — the mere passage of electricity is not
sufficient.

The muscle relaxant is used to prevent the normal movement of muscles that accompanies an epileptic fit, and therefore eliminates the risk of injury. When a muscle relaxant is
given, the fit is almost imperceptible, and not at all like the
lurid portrayals in films of the patient shaking violently on
a bed. In fact, there may be some difficulty in deciding if
the fit has occurred — the only signs may be the merest
twitch of the eyebrows or of the big toe. ECT given with
a relaxant in this way is called 'modified ECT', and is the
only method in routine use in this country.

The patient recovers consciousness within minutes. He or
she may have trouble remembering things after having the
treatment, but this will nearly always be temporary. This
memory disturbance tends to be seen more in elderly people.
A few patients may feel sick or suffer from headache or a stiff
neck. Although some patients need less, the usual practice is
to give eight to twelve shocks with a few days between each
shock.

ECT is occasionally given to **outpatients**. If so, your
relative will be told not to drink anything for some hours
beforehand. This is because an anaesthetic is given.
Following the treatment, he will be somewhat confused, but
will recover quickly. After an hour or so and a cup of tea,
he will be ready to be taken home by car or public transport.
In a few hours, he will be back to normal, except for a
difficulty in remembering things that may last a few days.

Sometimes, individual shocks have a marked effect in combating depression that wears off partly before the next shock is due. Recovery in such people follows a pattern of 'two steps forward, one step back'. Relatives should not worry about this rather jerky progress.

ECT has really had an extremely bad press. Recently a group of people were handing out leaflets to psychiatrists going into a meeting at the Royal Society of Medicine. The leaflets referred to psychiatrists 'frying people's brains'. Such views are extreme. However, some of the United States have banned the use of ECT, so the anti-ECT lobby clearly has a lot of support. It is likely that the effect of banning ECT in this country would not produce much change observable at the statistical level — the suicide rate might go up a bit, but it would be quite possible to put this down to other factors that have changed with the passage of time. We think, however, that at the individual level it would put some people through an unnecessarily prolonged period of extreme anguish. We sometimes see this now in hospitals where someone who falls clearly into the category that would get better from ECT is treated instead with antidepressants for a couple of months before the decision is finally taken to prescribe ECT — following which he or she improves rapidly.

Over the years there has been a lot of research on ECT. Although we do not know the precise details of how it works, we do know a lot about its effects and the indications for its use.

ECT has been shown to be a **safe** and **effective** treatment for severe depression, and psychiatrists use it because it may be the quickest way to reduce the patient's suffering or to overcome the risk of suicide. It can be used safely in the very old and in those who are quite ill physically. It may also be effective in cases of schizophrenia, but is now rarely prescribed because the major tranquillisers are used instead.

One of the main, although still relatively rare, complaints that patients make about ECT is that it impairs their memory. Again, there has been considerable research into this. When people who have had ECT are given memory tests there is no evidence of impairment — they are as good at remembering things as people who have not had ECT. So why do they say that their memory is not so good? There are indeed **short-lived** effects on memory, lasting perhaps a few weeks at most, and it is possible that people just find it hard to realise that these have got better. Sometimes, too, the people who feel their memory is bad turn out still to be depressed. As depressed people have poor registration and concentration, they commonly complain of poor memory, whether they have had ECT or not.

Martin was a 46-year-old divorced man who had recently returned from an executive post in the Middle East. He felt a bit flat, and low in spirits for a few weeks, perhaps even before he came back. His contract had been fairly lucrative, and he gradually came to believe that he had been overpaid, that a mistake had been made. He began to think that the authorities of the Middle Eastern country had found out about the overpayment, and were going to take legal action against him. He felt he had been culpable in not noticing the mistake himself, and that the authorities were justified in pursuing redress with the utmost rigor. He began to see himself as a worthless person, guilty of a heinous offence. One night he attempted to hang himself, and was only found by great good luck. When he was brought into hospital he was painfully agitated. He was prescribed antidepressants and placed under close observation. After four weeks there had been no improvement whatsoever, and the nurses suspected that he continued to be preoccupied with thoughts of suicide. It was decided to start ECT. After the first treatment, there was some slight but noticeable lightening in his mood, but this only lasted a couple of hours. He was kept under very close observation. After each treatment his mood improved for a time that gradually increased. After four weeks and eight treatments, Martin was very much better, although his mood still gave the impression of being a bit fragile. The ECT was stopped, but he gradually became somewhat depressed again, despite his antidepressant medication. It was decided to prescribe further ECT — after four more treatments, he was virtually back to his normal state and it was possible to discontinue it. He was able to take up his ordinary life again although, all told, he was in hospital for nearly six months.

Not everybody responds as well as this to ECT, although a majority with this sort of picture do so. However, it is experiences like this that convince many clinicians that ECT still has an important if occasional part to play in psychiatric treatment.

Psychosurgery

This has been used for certain psychiatric disorders. The commonest operation has been the **prefrontal leucotomy**, or **lobotomy** as it is sometimes called. The frontal part or **lobe** of the brain is just behind the forehead. The functions of this part of the brain are extremely subtle and it is possible to do without it both physically and socially. It is partly concerned with emotional responses, and the idea behind prefrontal leucotomy was to cut through the nerve connections that were responsible for this in order to change the intensity of mental suffering. The original operations were extremely crude, but nowadays radiation from radioactive needles placed in this part of the brain produces the same effect with much more precision. The radiation is very slight and only affects nerve cells very close to its source. The operation is very rarely carried out now, and only in centres which have special experience. It is used where suffering from depression is intolerable and virtually continuous and requires the patient to be in hospital more or less permanently. It does seem to help some people considerably. These days the main side effects of the operation are a loss of creativity, an inability to learn new skills and a degree of emotional coarsening or 'flattening'.

We must confess to very considerable worries about

psychosurgery, centring mainly on a distaste for producing permanent changes in someone's brain. In addition, although psychosurgery does appear to benefit some people experiencing extreme suffering, it has not really been properly evaluated, so we have no conclusive information about the balance of benefits and drawbacks, or the exact indications for its use.

Under the 1983 Mental Health Act, psychosurgery cannot be carried out without the patient's consent and the independent opinion of three specifically appointed people, one of whom is a doctor, that the consent is valid.

SOCIAL AND PSYCHOLOGICAL TREATMENTS

While patients are in hospital, and frequently after they return home, they will usually be offered some form of **social treatment**. This involves organising the various aspects of the **environment** in the most beneficial way. There are several ways of doing this, depending on the precise facilities available locally, and also to some extent on the views of local clinical staff about its usefulness for a particular individual.

As we described above, severe mental illness not only has the obvious effects such as suicidal ideas, hallucinations and loss of touch with reality, but less obvious and more persistent ones. These can cause equally difficult problems. Unlike a straightforward physical condition such as a broken leg or pneumonia, which people can observe and understand relatively easily, those suffering from severe mental illness usually look perfectly normal. This can make it hard for others, and indeed even the sufferer, to appreciate the unseen difficulties that may continue. These less obvious problems revolve around the **negative symptoms**, described on p. 44, such as slowness, poor concentration, tiredness, underactivity, loss of confidence in one's abilities, loss of interest in previous hobbies or friends, and an inability to show one's feelings. This may mean that your sick relative does not want, and is not immediately able, to return to a demanding

career or a full family life and responsibilities. Social treatments are designed to help in overcoming these difficulties
by providing a setting where people can be gradually encouraged to return to a previous level of outside interest and
function. It is important for all those concerned with the
patient's well-being to appreciate the special and unforeseen
problems that this transition can entail.

Occupational therapy (see also p. 89).
Most NHS hospitals have **occupational therapy departments** offering a range of activities that will help patients to
regain lost interests, skills and concentration, while allowing
them to feel that their time is creatively and usefully
employed during the day. These activities may be organised
in the department itself, or on the ward. Patients can find it
very helpful to have a timetable or structure to their day,
and to have somewhere to go apart from the ward or their
home. The activities offered may at first sight look much
too simple and undemanding both to you and to your ill
relative. This is because it may be hard, indeed even quite a
shock, to realise how poor his or her concentration or interest
has become. The activities are, in fact, carefully **graded** to
the individual's current capacity. The aim is to help sufferers
to regain skills steadily and gradually, and to minimise the
risk of failure which can be very discouraging to the
recovering patient. More complex and demanding tasks will
usually be provided, if patients become capable of them.
Sometimes the OT department will encourage totally new
interests, such as pottery, art, crafts or cookery, which patients can continue to develop. Your encouragement can be
very valuable here.

  Many of the activities centre on useful occupational or
domestic skills that can be employed to get someone back
into the swing of looking after herself. These are particularly
important when someone has been ill for an appreciable
period. Art and crafts are used to stimulate the sufferer and

permit a sense of creative achievement. Music, drama and dance may be used to enable patients to express themselves.

Tony was an intelligent man who had been admitted to hospital because of a severe depression. Because of this, he had little energy and could hardly be bothered to do anything. His psychiatrist and occupational therapist together worked out a daily programme with him. This was designed in such a way that he was encouraged to use what concentration he could muster, but very little pressure was put on him. Three of his sessions were in the pottery department, where it was suggested that he should try his hand at making relatively small, simple objects. He also helped with moving finished pottery around and doing other small tasks. Clearly the occupational therapist did not actually need his help in this way, but she kept him close by her for much of the time, encouraging him, talking to him and organising him. When he returned to the ward, he had the small satisfaction of having done something constructive, however trifling. This was the first stage in a plan to help Tony regain confidence and interest, and as he got better he was gradually led into doing more.

Industrial therapy
Hospital staff, and indeed patients themselves, may prefer a more **industrial setting** to re-establish confidence and concentration and to assist the return to work. Industrial therapy tends to be used for people who have had a longish period in hospital. As with occupational therapy, it can be helpful for the patient just to have a set time-table, to spend time out of the ward, and to have things to do and think about. Working alongside someone else can be beneficial, actually working with someone more so. Once more, the range of jobs — packing or light industrial work — may look far too simple, but is graded to the individual's capacity at the time. It may be that all someone can manage on a given day is to sit at his work place for half an hour.

Occupational and industrial therapy used to be the start

of a return to full-time **employment**. With current rates of
unemployment, the emphasis has now shifted to enabling
patients to regain lost skills, or to learn new skills if the
previous work record was poor. Industrial therapy also
provides a working environment where they can earn some
money, get used to the routine of a job again, and have
interesting activities to attend during the day. This may still
lead to a return to full or sheltered employment, but can also
be an end in itself.

Patrick had suffered from a series of depressive illnesses
and was also rather obsessive in his habits. This made him
slow, if very sure, in any task he might undertake. 'Slow
but sure' are not qualities suited to the needs of most jobs
these days, and he never managed to stay in work for very
long. Recent years had seen him unemployed for most of
the time. This did not help his tendency to depression or his
relationship with his ageing parents, with whom he lived.
Eventually, it was decided to offer him a place in an Industrial Therapy Unit. He tried out a number of tasks: the one
that most suited him had become available only recently in
the Unit, and consisted of entering statistical information
onto computer discs. Patrick's slowness did not matter too
much here, and his accuracy was appreciated. It does not
seem likely that he will ever work in open employment of
this type, but he has his place in the Unit, and is much more
cheerful. His parents appreciate the fact that he is no longer
moping around the house in the daytime, and family life is
much easier. In Patrick's case, industrial therapy has had an
important part in preventing an enduring and serious mental
problem from getting worse, and on this basis he can survive
in the community.

Group meetings
Some hospitals have regular meetings between staff and patients where patients' problems and experiences, both past and
present, may be discussed. While some patients say that they
find such meetings uncomfortable or boring, others find it

very valuable to be able to talk to or listen to others who understand their problems and have shared some of the same experiences. Not all hospitals place the same emphasis on group meetings. In some, they may be regarded as a central part of treatment and attention will be focused on events that happened to sufferers in childhood, in the belief that these are of crucial importance to the development of the patients' condition. It is then more likely to be referred to as **group therapy**. Groups in other hospitals may attend much more directly to everyday problems and how to solve them.

Individual therapy
Some patients will be offered time on their own with clinical staff to discuss their difficulties. As health professionals in hospitals now tend to work in teams, the staff member involved may be from any one of the variety of professions described on pp. 83–90. The sort of individual therapy offered can be extremely varied, from counselling about recent problems or specific programmes to help modify particular difficulties directly, to detailed sessions in which the relationship between earlier experiences and current problems is explored.

Sometimes only a few sessions are offered, in other cases, weekly sessions over several months or a year or two. The sort of help to be provided should be negotiated and agreed between the patient and the staff at the time. This treatment can be a great help to some people, by getting them to understand what has happened to them, how to prevent it happening again and how to cope in the future, should similar problems recur.

The regular opportunity to talk privately with a member of the clinical staff is often referred to as 'individual psycho-therapy', or just psychotherapy for short. It has also been called, somewhat jokingly but accurately, the 'talking treat-ment'. It takes a whole range of forms, and the procedure used by particular practitioners may follow quite closely from their adherence to a chosen theory of human psychology.

Psychoanalysis is a special type of psychotherapy, carried out along lines dictated by the beliefs of psychoanalytic theory. Psychoanalysts have always tended to form splinter groups, each with a different if related theory — so you get Freudian analysts, Jungian analysts, Kleinian analysts and so forth. All, however, share the opinion that earlier experiences determine later mental problems in a rather precise way.

Psychoanalysis started, as is well known, in central Europe, but is most influential in the United States, although its popularity there is now waning. There are some well-known British practitioners, but by and large most British psychiatrists are rather suspicious of elaborate theories that are supported by doubtful evidence. They prefer to keep things relatively simple, and will only take as a fact what has been clearly established — although they are perhaps readier to accept biological ideas than psychological ones, probably as a consequence of their medical training. In psychological matters, they are more influenced by the rather different theories of their clinical psychologist colleagues.

Members of the public often do not realise this, and are rather surprised to find that psychiatrists are more concerned with current practical difficulties than with probing the deep recesses of the mind. While there is no doubt about the pervasive influence of psychoanalytic ideas, and psychiatrists readily recognise that early experiences are likely to be important in shaping the way people behave in adult life, they tend to think that not a lot can be done to change what has already happened. Psychoanalysts, in contrast, think that very early experience can affect later life by influencing it in ways that the individual does not know about, and that bringing these influences into consciousness can help to destroy them.

Most psychotherapy carried out in the National Health Service is 'supportive psychotherapy', concentrating on everyday problems, although with some attempt to give the patient insight into his or her behaviour. Psychologists may offer psychotherapy of this type, but also provide special types called 'behavioural psychotherapy' or the increasingly influential 'cognitive psychotherapy'.

Cognitive therapy is based on the idea that people's emotional states depend on their attitudes to things going on around them. Depressed people are locked into a gloomy misinterpretation of events and of the light they cast on the sufferer that has become automatic and therefore difficult to shift. The therapist points out these habitual attitudes to the patient, and helps him monitor his style of thinking. Making these processes more conscious gives the patient the chance of changing them to more appropriate and beneficial ones. This relatively new treatment seems to be quite successful in treating depressions of at least moderate severity, and carries the prospect of helping to keep patients well once they have recovered, as they can themselves spot and deal with any tendency to slip back into old ways. However, as yet it is not widely available.

Social workers often refer to their psychotherapeutic effort as 'casework', and in some instances this will have been influenced by psychoanalytic ideas.

Family therapy
This is a more recent form of social treatment developed since the 1970s. Whole families are asked to meet together with one, or sometimes two, professional staff to discuss areas of difficulty. This form of treatment is appropriate if the sufferers are in close contact with their families, as their relatives are then likely to continue to be involved in their care. Again, family meetings are offered by staff as individual circumstances dictate: they may be limited to one or two occasions, or continue over some months or years. Some families find it extremely useful to look at how they get on together, to understand why difficulties have occurred in the

past and to consider how they might help each other cope
with problems.

Relatives' groups

As yet, these are offered routinely by very few NHS hospitals. Most such groups are actually **self-help groups** organised by interested relatives to enable them to share problems
and support each other. The **National Schizophrenia
Fellowship** is the best known of these organisations in the
UK and is worth describing in some detail — you may find
that what it offers is useful to you.

The National Schizophrenia Fellowship provides a variety
of services for relatives. Obviously, some of these are more
or less restricted to those who became members of the organisation. Participation in local NSF groups provides information about local services but also, more importantly
perhaps, personal support and the exchange of information
about problems of caring. Membership also gives access to
various projects the local groups may have set up, including
outings, holidays, housing, sheltered employment, social
clubs and day centres. The group can provide 'muscle' to
back up individual members' dissatisfactions or complaints,
and knowledgeable NSF members in local areas can be tele-
phoned for support.

In addition, NSF headquarters offers an advisory service,
which is available to all. This supplies information and advice
about housing, holidays, employment, benefits and other
services provided by the statutory, voluntary and private
sectors. There is also a library of video and audio-tapes
covering much of current expert opinion about schizophrenia. There are lists of publications helpful to relatives,
some of which are produced by the Fellowship itself.

Advice is available about complaints procedures. Indeed,
the NSF will take up specific problems with the statutory
services if the relative's own attempts have been unsuccessful. This service is limited by the availability of personnel
and so may give priority to actual members. The sort of

problems that the NSF often has to deal with are the threat-
ened or actual discharge home of a still unwell patient to a
relative who cannot cope, the refusal of hospital admission
to a very sick person at home, lack of information about
medication and its likely side effects, an inadequate service
from the family doctor, and general dissatisfaction with
psychiatrist services. The NSF also represents relatives' and
carers' views to policy makers and service providers (Health
Authorities, Local Authorities, Government, professional
bodies). They campaign and lobby on issues brought to their
attention by relatives.

The **Manic Depression Fellowship** is a relatively new
organization for those who suffer from manic depressive
illness and their relatives. For a small annual fee, it offers
to members a quarterly newsletter, occasional factsheets,
meetings and, perhaps most especially, assistance in setting
up local self-help groups. There are about sixty of these so
far, and the organisation is expanding. Compared with the
NSF, a larger proportion of members are actual sufferers.

MIND's local associations sometimes can and do act as
support groups for troubled relatives.

ALTERNATIVE MEDICINE AND PSYCHIATRY
You may come across other treatments for which claims are
made, such as special diets and the use of ionisers. Distressed
patients and their relatives may be dissatisfied with the
response to routine therapy, particularly if it does not seem
to improve things much, and are sometimes willing to place
their faith in something that appears to offer an alternative.
Unfortunately, such treatments are sometimes proposed by
uncritical enthusiasts, and sometimes by those with a strong
financial interest in promoting them.

Practitioners in this area are now organising themselves
into societies that will establish standards of practice and
methods of investigating the effectiveness of their treatments. Nevertheless, we have considerable reservations, and
feel that relatives should be cautious about unconventional

treatments of this sort. In our view, it would be more useful if your dissatisfaction with the service your sick relative is getting led you to press for better services of the conventional kind.

5   Legal Matters

The most important part of this chapter deals with the rules which have to be followed in arranging **compulsory admission** and **compulsory treatment**, and the safeguards which exist. Only about one person in twenty is admitted to a mental hospital under compulsion, so in the large majority of cases relatives will not require this information. However, for those of you who do, we have given it in some detail. Rather than summarise all the mental health legislation, we have concentrated on those parts most likely to be relevant to people living with sufferers from schizophrenia and manic depressive illness.

The rights of patients and relatives

Most admissions to hospital happen because patients and their doctors agree this is the best way to deal with the patients' difficulties. This is known as **informal** or **voluntary admission**. Patients are always given the opportunity to agree to an admission the psychiatrist thinks is necessary. Sometimes, however, patients may need to be admitted to, or detained in, hospital against their will. In Britain, we have always been careful to defend the rights of individuals, and **compulsory admission** is a legal process with legal safeguards. The law in England and Wales has recently been revised in the **1983 Mental Health Act**. Under this Act, the nearest relative of a compulsorily detained patient has both rights and duties, and may be involved in the admission

137

procedure. New Acts along similar lines are now law in Scotland and Northern Ireland.

The rights of voluntary patients

Voluntary admission to hospital is by mutual agreement of the sufferer and the medical team. Under these circumstances, patients have the right to refuse treatment and to discharge themselves. However, if your relative refuses to comply with the recommended plan of treatment, this undermines the alliance between him or her and the medical team. The sufferer must therefore weigh the pros and cons of downright refusal of treatment or of discharge against medical advice. It is much better to try to discuss the problems with staff in order to find a mutually acceptable solution. In extreme cases, the team may decide to discharge the patient if she is not co-operating with plans for treatment, and may even refuse to continue seeing her as an outpatient, on the grounds that it has become impossible to do so. However, this is relatively unlikely where the patient is clearly suffering from the consequences of a severe mental illness like schizophrenia or manic depressive illness.

If a patient does decide that she wants to discharge herself against medical advice, she may be asked to sign a statement to that effect. This might be used in the light of subsequent developments to protect the medical team from allegations of negligence.

In some cases, people agree to be admitted on a voluntary basis even though they may be seriously disturbed and a potential danger to themselves or others. If they then change their minds and want to discharge themselves, the medical team may well decide that they must remain in the hospital on a compulsory basis. In other cases, someone may deteriorate in hospital despite the attentions of staff, and this may also lead the team to consider compulsory detention, particularly if the patient is refusing a needed treatment. This state of affairs does give considerable powers to psychiatrists, about which you and your sick relative may feel uneasy. In most cases the powers are used for the genuine benefit of the patient and there are safeguards, which we describe below.

The patient's nearest relative
The nearest relative is the one with whom the patient lived before going into hospital. Where there is more than one such person or the patient lives alone, the **legal nearest relative** is the one closest to the top of the list in Table 9.

TABLE 9
Nearest Relatives

husband/wife
son/daughter
father/mother
brother/sister
grandparent
grandchild
uncle/aunt
nephew/niece

A cohabitee may qualify as the nearest relative if he or she has lived with the patient for at least six months as husband or wife, but does not take over the rights of the actual husband or wife unless there has been a legal separation or divorce. A person other than a relative who has lived with the patient for at least five years counts as a relative, but in the last position on the list.

Who can be admitted or detained against their will?
Compulsory procedures can only be used to admit or detain patients suffering from certain types of disorder. The rules governing this are laid down in the 1983 Act. The person must be suffering from a **mental disorder** sufficiently severe to make admission appropriate, and must have **refused**

voluntary admission. The admission must be in the interests
of the patient's own health or safety, or for the protection
of others. 'Mental disorder' covers three conditions: mental
illness, psychopathic disorder, and mental impairment (basically mental handicap); but **excludes** sexual deviation and
dependence on alcohol or drugs. Slightly different powers
apply to each of these three conditions. Those suffering from
'mental illness' are subject to the widest powers. The British
Acts do not define what is meant by this term, although the
Northern Irish one does, but it would clearly cover both
schizophrenia and manic depressive illness. Compulsory
admission is most commonly used for suicidal patients, for
those who harbour beliefs of persecution, and for those who
are incapable of looking after themselves physically or who
may cause themselves untold social damage, running up
huge debts and the like.

Admission and detention under the Mental Health Act
There are different sections of the Act describing the proper
procedures for use in particular circumstances. The duration
of detention varies according to the procedure used, and the
recommendation for detention can be renewed when it runs
out. There are particular rules, for patients admitted
following criminal proceedings, that are not discussed here.

Under Section 136 of the Act, people suspected of being
a danger to themselves or others and found in a public place,
can be taken to a 'place of safety' by a **police officer**.
Usually, a place of safety means a hospital, making it relatively easy for the patient to be assessed by a doctor and an
approved social worker. This must be done within 72 hours.
A 'place of safety' can mean a residential home or a police
station, but these are less suitable and less commonly used.

Under Section 135, an approved social worker can apply
to a Magistrate to issue a warrant for premises to be searched
for people suspected of being mentally disordered. There
must be grounds for believing that they are being mistreated
or neglected, or are alone and unable to care for themselves.

The warrant is carried out by a police officer, accompanied by a social worker and a doctor.

However, these circumstances are relatively unusual. A commoner situation arises when, because of a disturbance indoors, at home or elsewhere, someone calls the **family doctor**, who thinks the patient should be admitted but cannot persuade him or her to enter hospital voluntarily. The procedure then requires an **application**, which can be signed either by a specially approved social worker or by the nearest relative. There also has to be one or more **medical recommendation**. If there is only one such recommendation, this permits an **emergency admission**, under **Section 4** of the Act. In this case the medical recommendation should preferably be from a doctor who knows the patient, most usually his or her GP. The patient can only be held for 72 hours, unless another doctor is obtained within this period to make an additional recommendation, thus converting it to a Section 2 admission (see below). A social worker signing the application form without the knowledge of the nearest relative must, with all urgency, tell the relative what has happened. Both the doctor and the social worker must have seen the patient within 24 hours of signing their part of the Section.

Admission for assessment requires the recommendations of *two* doctors, and one of them must be recognised as having special psychiatric expertise. This type of admission is permitted by **Section 2** of the Act, and the compulsory power lasts for 28 days.

Patients who have been admitted compulsorily can be stopped from leaving the hospital by staff, and if they do leave they can be brought back. If they are not brought back within 28 days, however, this power is lost.

Admission for treatment is governed by **Section 3** of the Act. This lasts for up to six months, but can then be renewed for a further six months. After that it can be renewed annually. Under Section 3, if the nearest relative objects, the social worker cannot make the application.

However, if the social worker thinks the relative is being unreasonable, he may apply to a County Court for the nearest relative's function to be transferred to someone else, who need not be another relative.

There may be circumstances in which you feel your ill relative needs compulsory admission. One way of doing this is by calling the family doctor, and yourself signing the application. Another way is to ask the local social services department to arrange for an approved social worker to consider the case. If satisfied that compulsory admission cannot be avoided, the social worker will then make an application under the Act. If the social worker does not think compulsory admission is justified, he must inform you in writing.

There are also powers under **Section 5** of the Act that can be used by designated doctors and nurses to prevent a patient from leaving, even when she originally agreed to go into hospital voluntarily. Once more, it must be thought that the patient is a danger to herself or others. This power to detain is important, because otherwise the patient would have to be allowed to leave, and might experience considerable suffering or damage before the procedures of Section 4 could be arranged.

Details of the sections of the 1983 Mental Health Act that govern compulsory admission procedures are summarised in Table 10.

Safeguards following a compulsory admission
It is possible for the compulsory powers to be revoked before they run out. Usually this is done by the doctor in charge of the patient. For instance, the doctor may revoke an emergency section (Section 4), feeling that although it was a reasonable course of action at the time, it now looks to have been inappropriately applied. In other cases, the patient has asked for the compulsory order to be suspended. He or she may be considerably better and in any case likely to be reasonably co-operative with treatment, either as an informal inpatient

TABLE 10
1983 Mental Health Act Part II: Compulsory admission

Section	Purpose	Applicant	Medical recommendation	Duration	Outcome
4	Emergency assessment (mental disorder)	Nearest relative or approved social worker (who must have seen the patient within the previous 24 hours)	Any doctor	72 hours	Discharge of order: by lapse; by consultant; by managers; by nearest relative. Conversion to Section 2 by second medical recommendation
2	Assessment (mental disorder)	Nearest relative or approved social worker who must attempt to inform the nearest relative	Two doctors, one approved under the Mental Health Act as having special expertise in psychiatry	28 days	Discharge of order: by lapse; by consultant; by managers; by nearest relative. Conversion to Section 3.
3	Treatment (i) Mental illness or severe mental impairment (ii) Psychopathic disorder or mental impairment if treatable	Nearest relative or approved social worker, provided that he has attempted to consult the nearest relative who must consent	Two doctors, as above, giving reasons for detention, form of disorder and consideration of other methods of dealing with the patient	6 months renewable for a further 6 months, then at yearly intervals	Discharge of order: by lapse; by consultant; by managers; by nearest relative; by MHRT

or as an outpatient. In such cases, the doctor will often be happy to agree, feeling that treatment by mutual consent is more pleasant, and more likely to be effective.

The **Hospital Managers** can also revoke compulsory powers. The Hospital Managers are actually the **District Health Authority** but are usually represented by the hospital's **chief administrator**. If the patient requests the doctor to discontinue her compulsory detention and the doctor refuses, she may ask the hospital managers to discharge her. A Managers' Hearing will then be arranged, attended by members of the District Health Authority, and this may confirm the patient's discharge.

If a patient is discharged from compulsory detention, the nearest relative must be informed, unless either he or the patient has requested otherwise.

Patients also have the right to appear before a **Mental Health Review Tribunal**, which may order their release. The Hospital Managers have a duty to inform compulsorily detained patients about their rights and, in particular, about their right of appeal to these Tribunals. Provided the patient agrees, the Managers must also inform the nearest relative of these rights, and the relative can also apply to the Tribunal for the patient to be reviewed. The application must be in writing. Patients can ask to be **represented** at the Tribunal by a friend or relative, or by a lawyer. MIND (the National Association for Mental Health — see address in the Appendix) offers help with representation. Legal aid is available if necessary, but the representation organised by MIND is usually free anyway.

These tribunals are independent bodies that ensure that people admitted to hospital are not being kept there unnecessarily. Each Regional Health Authority in England has one, and there is one for the whole of Wales. The hearings are conducted by a **president**, who is a lawyer, with one medical and one lay colleague to help. The main duty of tribunals is to decide whether a person can be released from hospital. They can also order a patient to be discharged at some future date. They can compel witnesses to attend, and take evidence under oath. Hearings are usually in private, although the patient or relative can request a public hearing.

Patients are only allowed to apply to tribunals at certain intervals. As you might suspect, there is no right of appeal to the tribunal where detention is compelled under those sections of the Act, such as Section 4, that only hold for 72 hours. Details are given in Tables 11 and 12.

If you are the nearest relative, you can discharge a patient held under the powers of the Mental Health Act. It requires 72 hours' notice in writing to the Hospital Managers, so the power obviously does not apply to those sections of the Act that only empower detention for 72 hours. The medical officer in charge of treatment can countermand your powers of discharge, but this in turn must be done in writing, and you can then refer your sick relative to a Mental Health Review Tribunal.

MIND's legal department will always advise you, and the organisation's booklet *A Mental Health Review Tribunal May Help You* explains how to apply. You should be able to get this from your hospital social worker, the local Community Health Council, the Citizens' Advice Bureau or through MIND itself.

Compulsory treatment

In cases of acute emergency, any patient can be given medication without his or her consent, although the treatment given must be appropriate to the scale of the emergency. Indeed this is actually spelt out by the Mental Health Act for compulsorily detained patients. In other situations, voluntary patients can only be treated if they agree to it: they have the right to refuse under common law. Legal consent to treatment does not just mean agreeing to it. The doctor must explain the nature, purpose and effect of the treatment and the patient must be of sound enough mind to understand it. However, there is no formal procedure for obtaining a voluntary patient's consent to drug treatment —

TABLE 11
Periods of eligibility for Mental Health Review Tribunals

Mental Health Act 1983	First 14 days	First 6 months	Second 6 months	Annually
Sections 4, 5, 136 (72 hours)	✓	—	—	—
Section 2 (28 days)	—	✓	—	—
Section 3 (treatment order)	—	✓	✓	✓
Section 37 (hospital order)	—	—	✓	✓
Sections 37 and 41 (hospital order with restriction order)	—	—	✓	✓

TABLE 12
Automatic Mental Health Review Tribunals

Mental Health Act 1983	First 6 months	Second 6 months	Every 3 years
Section 3 (treatment order)	—	✓	✓
Section 37 (hospital order)	—	—	✓
Sections 37 and 41 (hospital order with restriction order)	—	—	✓

if he or she accepts the doctor's prescription, it is assumed that this indicates consent. ECT is regarded as the equivalent of a minor operation, and so patients are required to sign a consent form (see p. 122). Where voluntary patients are so mentally disturbed that they cannot understand the nature of the treatment offered, the doctor is really obliged to convert their admission into a compulsory one.

Patients who are compulsorily detained are often able to consent to treatment in the normal way. However, they can be treated against their will in certain circumstances. However, **ECT** and **long-lasting courses of medicine** can only be given on the strength of an **independent second medical opinion**, that is, the opinion of a doctor who does not work in the same hospital as the consultant responsible. Under the new Act, treatment involving brain surgery or the implantation of hormones to lower male sexual drive can never be given without the patient's consent. Any patient can withdraw consent to treatment at any time. The psychiatrist's decision to embark on compulsory treatment of a detained patient is then governed by the safeguards of the Mental Health Act. The cases of patients who are being treated compulsorily are monitored by the new **Mental Health Commission** set up under the 1983 Act. This is an independent body made up of legal and medical professionals and lay people and responsible to the Secretary of State. Members visit hospitals once or twice a year and ensure the correct working of the 1983 Mental Health Act. At the time a detention order is due for renewal, the doctor in charge of the patient's case must report to the Commission on his or her condition and the progress of treatment. The Commission may itself request such a report at any time, and has the power to withdraw the authority for compulsory treatment.

Patients' mail
Except for patients in 'special' hospitals like Broadmoor, mail **from** a patient cannot be intercepted unless the person

to whom it is addressed has asked for this **in writing**. The patient has to be informed of the interception by the hospital authorities, again in writing. Mail to a patient in an ordinary psychiatric hospital cannot be intercepted.

Complaining about treatment or the use of compulsory powers
You or your sick relative may complain, either during admission or later, about any aspect of treatment. In addition to the normal channels open to the citizen (such as writing to Members of Parliament, Ministers of the Crown, the Parliamentary Commissioner, the Health Service Commissioner or the local Community Health Council) there are **three** special sources of redress for patients and their relatives. The Hospital Managers should be approached first, and only if you are still not satisfied should you take things further. The Mental Health Review Tribunals have already been mentioned on p. 144. In addition, relatives and patients may apply to the Mental Health Commission described above. The Commission may be contacted by letter, or directly when members are visiting the hospital. Patients can complain about any incident they are unhappy about, but relatives may themselves contact the Commission only about procedures under the powers of the Mental Health Act — basically, compulsory admission or treatment. The Commission may deal with a complaint directly or, under certain circumstances, by referring it to other procedures set up for the purpose. In future, they may also take over responsibility for informal patients' interests as well.

In Scotland and Northern Ireland, the procedures covering compulsory admission and treatment are laid down in separate Acts of Parliament. These are similar in principle to, but differ in detail from, the Mental Health Act that applies in England and Wales. If you live in those areas, you may obtain guidance about the local legislation from local branches of MIND, or from the hospital to which your relative has been admitted.

In Scotland, applications for compulsory admission must be submitted to a Sheriff. There are no Mental Health Review Tribunals, but the Scottish equivalent of the Mental Health Commission, called the Mental Welfare Commission, has responsibility for reviewing and, if appropriate, discharging patients. It also looks after the interests of voluntary patients.

The Mental Health Commission for Northern Ireland also has the duty of reviewing the care and treatment of all mentally disordered people. However, it cannot discharge them. This can only be done by the NI Mental Health Review Tribunal.

Finally, a detained patient can **sue** for compensation, if the motive for detaining him was improper, or if the doctors were negligent in making their medical recommendations. He can sue anyone involved in the process — the doctors, social workers, nurses, or indeed the nearest relative. However, he needs the permission of the High Court to bring a civil action, and of the Director of Public Prosecutions to bring a criminal action.

Wills and contracts

Everyone knows that wills always start off with references to 'being of sound mind'. In fact, the person making the will only has to be of sound enough mind to know what his particular will means. He has to know what property he has, who has a claim on it, and what the relative strengths of those claims are. The will must be legible and unambiguous. Solicitors may seek medical opinion on their client's state of mind.

Contracts require a sound mind in the same way that wills do. Marriage is a contract, and in theory would be void if one of the partners was at the time incapable of understanding the nature and responsibilities of marriage. More usually, marriages are regarded as voidable, not because a partner was incapable of giving consent, but because he was suffering from a mental disorder of such a nature and extent as to unfit him for marriage.

Other rights and duties
For most people admission to hospital is temporary and they can vote as from their home address. For patients staying longer, a general hospital or nursing home can be used as an address for the purposes of the electoral roll. However, a mental hospital is *not* a valid address. Compulsory patients cannot vote.

People seeing a doctor for treatment of a mental illness are excused **jury service**.

If someone becomes aware of any disability that is likely to affect his ability to **drive**, he is obliged to inform the Driver and Vehicle Licensing Centre. Mental illness is such a disability, although it is not stipulated what sort of illness. Clearly, people who are acutely ill with schizophrenia or manic depressive disorder should not drive. Fortunately, they do not usually attempt it. Problems are more likely if your relative is recovering, and you may not be sure if it is a good idea for him to drive, particularly if he is taking medication. Most psychiatric medication interferes to some extent with the ability to drive. If in doubt it may be a good plan to talk to your relative's doctor about the problem. In extreme cases, if you cannot persuade your relative not to drive, you yourself may have to contact the DVLC. The doctor is unlikely to do this as it would involve a breach of professional confidence.

things worse. She said, 'I realised it was no good,
ued to be more patient.' This was without anyone's
r help, she just learned with the passage of time that
ngs were helpful, and other things made life harder.
re patient and tolerant attitude, expecting a little less
 becoming so angry, made the atmosphere much
etween them, and helped her sister to recover faster
 illness.

cond important principle that may help you cope is
 to have **your own interests** and continue to lead
vn life if you wish to. It is quite possible to be
y caring and supportive whilst maintaining your
side interests, going to work and going on holiday.
ery often feel they should give all this up: it is
o feel that you should not leave your ill relative
home just to go out and enjoy yourself. However,
is to be a mistake. Those who are able to lead their
s to some extent and who do not become totally
d in looking after their sick relative, do feel better
es, but also, very crucially, allow the sufferer some
lence. In our experience, relatives who have lived
ntally ill people for many years very rarely have a
 However, if they start going out sometimes,
even going to work, if only part-time, or doing
ings by themselves and for themselves, this can
ue balance and reduce the tendency to do too much
ther person, rather than just enough.
ouple were very worried that, if they left their son
the house for any length of time, he would set fire
tchen while making himself a cup of tea. In fact this
ly happened on several occasions in the past, so it
an unrealistic fear. However, after safeguarding the
as much as possible beforehand, they tried a few
vay from home. No disaster happened, and it was
to build on this in an attempt to restore some of
le's own life and enjoyment together.
d to the necessity of doing things that are for your

6 Looking Afte

Coping with yourself

This may not seem an obvious asp
about, and it is easily overlooked.
on your relative, mentally ill and
feelings or problems can be for
This is a great pity, and indeed
book.

Living and coping with an indiv
mental illness can be rewarding, w
Often, however, this is not the ca
your own reactions may be cru
with problems effectively and
developing. Individuals with sor
particularly schizophrenia, can be
family atmosphere. If you ar
with the difficulties that arise, t
arguments avoided.

The first important thing to be
one's interest for you to try to d
and **with tolerance**, even if you
calm. This helps sufferers to r
indeed, keeps them well.

For example, a sister who wa
had become ill, described how
impatient and irritated by her
inability to do various things, or
time passed, however, she real

mak
so I
adv
som
This
and
calm
from

T
the
you
extre
own
Peop
natur
alone
this s
own
imme
them
indep
with
holida
perha
other
restor
for the

One
alone
to the
had no
was no
kitche
hours
possibl
this co
Rela

6　Looking After Yourself

Coping with yourself

This may not seem an obvious aspect for you to be concerned about, and it is easily overlooked. The focus may be so much on your relative, mentally ill and vulnerable, that your own feelings or problems can be forgotten or not recognised. This is a great pity, and indeed one of the reasons for this book.

Living and coping with an individual who has had a severe mental illness can be rewarding, with no particular problems. Often, however, this is not the case, particularly at first, and your own reactions may be crucial to your ability to deal with problems effectively and to prevent crises from developing. Individuals with some severe mental illnesses, particularly schizophrenia, can be especially sensitive to the **family atmosphere**. If you are able to cope effectively with the difficulties that arise, tension will be reduced and arguments avoided.

The first important thing to be learnt is that it is in everyone's interest for you to try to deal with difficulties **calmly** and **with tolerance**, even if you are not feeling particularly calm. This helps sufferers to recover more quickly and, indeed, keeps them well.

For example, a sister who was living with her twin who had become ill, described how initially she had been very impatient and irritated by her behaviour, particularly her inability to do various things, or help around the house. As time passed, however, she realised that this attitude was

151

making things worse. She said, 'I realised it was no good, so I learned to be more patient.' This was without anyone's advice or help, she just learned with the passage of time that some things were helpful, and other things made life harder. This more patient and tolerant attitude, expecting a little less and not becoming so angry, made the atmosphere much calmer between them, and helped her sister to recover faster from the illness.

The second important principle that may help you cope is the need to have **your own interests** and continue to lead **your own life** if you wish to. It is quite possible to be extremely caring and supportive whilst maintaining your own outside interests, going to work and going on holiday. People very often feel they should give all this up: it is natural to feel that you should not leave your ill relative alone at home just to go out and enjoy yourself. However, this seems to be a mistake. Those who are able to lead their own lives to some extent and who do not become totally immersed in looking after their sick relative, do feel better themselves, but also, very crucially, allow the sufferer some independence. In our experience, relatives who have lived with mentally ill people for many years very rarely have a holiday. However, if they start going out sometimes, perhaps even going to work, if only part-time, or doing other things by themselves and for themselves, this can restore the balance and reduce the tendency to do too much for the other person, rather than just enough.

One couple were very worried that, if they left their son alone in the house for any length of time, he would set fire to the kitchen while making himself a cup of tea. In fact this had nearly happened on several occasions in the past, so it was not an unrealistic fear. However, after safeguarding the kitchen as much as possible beforehand, they tried a few hours away from home. No disaster happened, and it was possible to build on this in an attempt to restore some of this couple's own life and enjoyment together.

Related to the necessity of doing things that are for your

own satisfaction, in the process allowing your ill relative some independence at times, is the danger of being too protective. Sufferers are normally adults, even if they have not all managed to achieve much independent adult life, and it can be too easy to go back to treating them as children — unable to be left to themselves, to look after themselves or to make their own decisions. It is quite true that at various stages in the severe mental illnesses, sufferers may lose the ability to look after themselves properly, or lose contact with reality and not care about such things. However, this state is not normally permanent, and it is all too easy for you to get into the habit of doing and organising all the things that need to be done.

In one family, Carl was able to cook a meal and do some cleaning and shopping, but it was easier and more efficient for his 70-year-old mother to do it all for both of them. It took some time and effort to establish that Carl should do more than he did round the house, and to decide that he should be responsible for at least one meal a week. Once this was achieved it was possible to build on it, so that Carl felt that he had achieved something and was of some use around the house, and his mother could begin to share some of the responsibilities she had always taken on alone.

The third important principle in coping with mental illness in the family is to avoid being too **intrusive**. While it is not a good idea to leave your ill relative totally alone and isolated, particularly as these illnesses have in any case a tendency to make the sufferer withdraw from other people, it is also useful to know when to leave someone alone. One mother said, 'I follow him around the house, I'm so worried what he'll do next.' While it is understandable and natural to worry, and while it may be necessary at times of acute illness to be very observant when there is a risk of suicide, this level of worry, anger or upset may continue even when the illness is a little better. At this stage it can be very wearing for you, and quite destructive if you have no relief. It may also prevent you developing more tolerant and realistic attitudes. It is often desirable for the sufferer to be able to go and lie down in his own room for a while, as he may frequently be oversensitive to the presence of other people and feel he simply has to be left alone sometimes. One mother said, 'I know he gets upset at times and he goes to his bedroom. I don't go in for a while, just leave him; then, later on, I'll offer him a cup of tea, take it in to him if he won't come down, and ask if things are any better.' A wife whose husband's inactivity made her very angry, as she had to take on all the household chores, childcare and a part-time job, said, 'Sometimes I just go for a walk round the park to get away from him for a while. It means I can calm down and feel better when I go back in.'

Those who cope successfully with the problems of a sick relative have usually come to recognise both what is helpful and what is not. It often happens that expectations of a sufferer's future performance or life-style have to change. It can be tragic to watch a much loved son or daughter fall short of early hopes, or to see a partner unable to match the initial promise of a relationship. Many parents and spouses talk of a time similar to that following bereavement, and equally painful, when these adjustments take place in their hopes and expectations, although they should be tactful about sharing these feelings with the sufferer.

Particularly if you are a partner, you are likely at one time or another to feel that you want to end the relationship. This is being realistic, and probably happens to every couple at some stage. In some cases it is the best outcome, and sufferers and their families manage better with less frequent and less intense contact, particularly if this has been very upsetting in the past. Hospital staff often suggest that grown-up children do not return home to live full-time with their parents but go to a hostel, or sheltered housing, or their own flat. It may be a better and much more realistic long-term solution to keep in a degree of contact of your own choosing with a suffer living elsewhere, than to be forced to continue to live together when problems are insurmountable. Such decisions should only be made after discussion between you, your sick relative and the hospital staff.

For some people, the only compensation for caring for their sick relative comes from a sense of duty done. While this deserves respect, it should not blind them to what may be best for the patient where, for example, home circumstances are so fraught that a separation would be the best answer. Those who feel there are few rewards for caring for a sick person should take particular care that other aspects of their lives compensate. One relative wisely advises, 'in order to cope with sometimes unbearable strain, you must keep well, eat well, get as much sleep and exercise as you can. Try to keep up with your work and hobbies, and try to find support in what you can — religion, friendship, a sense of mission. Do not hide your difficulties from relatives and friends: if you do, they will think you do not need their sympathy.'

The future

You may be able to retain an optimistic attitude to the future, to view things calmly and deal with problems as they arise. On the other hand you may well feel pessimistic, see no way of changing things and expect grave and insoluble problems to persist. These attitudes tend to be self-fulfilling.

If your sick relative can accept treatment from clinical staff, if you encourage this and remain calm about crises, and if there are few additional problems such as financial hardship, an initially fraught situation may eventually become acceptable, routine and even quite satisfying. Then you may worry about becoming older: 'What will happen when I am gone?' This is often a realistic fear, as many caring relatives, particularly parents, provide such high levels of support that they cannot be replaced. Ideally, part of the care that you provide should aim to enable the sufferer (as any other adult) to become as independent as possible. Keeping links with other family members and friends may be important for you, but also ensures the sufferer has others

to turn to at times. It is also sensible to make sure your
relative does not lose domestic skills or the ability to look
after himself. Help with this is often provided by hospital
occupational therapy departments, and they should be
encouraged to participate in this.

It is important to remember that, in time, most sick relatives either recover from their illness or become adapted to
its effects. Individual sufferers may learn what can upset
them and begin to avoid it or in other ways reduce its effects.
With sympathetic medical care, they may come to accept
that medication has a useful role to play in the control of
their illness and to comply with a dosage that has the fewest
possible side effects. Many sufferers will recover completely.
Others will eventually be able to reduce or stop medication.
In time, your relative and you can often become adept at
recognising the warning signs of an impending relapse and
obtaining prompt treatment for it, thus reducing the length
and upset of later bouts of illness. Many individuals and
their carers are also able to say that such illnesses provide
experiences others can never have and have added to their
lives in unexpectedly fulfilling ways.

Holidays
These can be a very important source of relief for those
living with someone suffering from a mental illness. After
all, it can be a full-time job, and other workers are entitled
to periods of leave. Separate holidays are the ideal, at least
on occasion, and you should not feel guilty about this — it
also gives your relative a break from you!

Some social services departments will organise holidays
for the mentally ill, and you may find out about other possibilities from the Psychiatric Rehabilitation Association or the
Holiday Care Service (see Appendix). Your relative may
lack the energy or motivation to do this, so you may have
to arrange the holiday for him. It may be possible to get
financial help if you and your relative are on a low income.

You may feel it is difficult to go off on holiday on your

own. Sometimes, this feeling may be misplaced: your relative might well be able, and indeed happy, to manage on
his own for a week or two. Sometimes, it may be realistic
for you to feel that he could not manage. In such circumstances, you might be able to persuade another relative,
either to come and live with the sufferer, or to have to stay
while you are on holiday. You may need to make it clear
that it is not a permanent arrangement! In some cases, your
relative's psychiatric team may be sympathetic and arrange,
say, a fortnight's relief admission so that you can go on
holiday — after all, this is a very efficient use of a hospital bed, to support someone undertaking much of the responsibility for caring for a mentally ill person. In other areas the
team may not have thought much about the needs of the
relatives of their patients. Nevertheless, if you make the
suggestion to them, they may feel it is not an unreasonable
idea. The local social services department may also be able
to help.

Getting further advice and information
We have mentioned many of these sources of support
already.
   Information about local NHS facilities may be available
from your family doctor, although it must be said that there
are some who are less well informed than they might be.
The psychiatric team dealing with your relative are perhaps
a more reliable source, and the team's social worker might
be the best person to contact. One way of finding out about
the available facilities is to ask to discuss the plans for
managing your relative's illness now they have returned to
the community, a reasonable request in view of the fact that
you will be providing some of the care.
   Other agencies that provide information about local facilities include the local social services departments, the Citizens'
Advice Bureau, the Community Health Council, your local
branch of MIND, and the Patients' Association.
   Information about employment for the mentally ill can be

obtained from the Disablement Resettlement Officer at your local job centre, who will also know about facilities for employment rehabilitation.

The National Schizophrenia Fellowship, set up by relatives of people with this condition, can be a great source of support as well as of information (see also pp. 134–5). MIND (the National Association for Mental Health) are very good at meeting requests for information, and have a range of booklets about particular topics. The Mental Health Foundation, who commissioned this book, also have booklets and publications concerning related subjects. Several books give information about financial benefits. These include the *Disability Rights Handbook* of the Disability Alliance Educational and Research Association, and the *National Welfare Benefits Handbook* and *Rights Guide to non Means Tested Social Security Benefits*, published by the Child Poverty Action Group.

The names and addresses of more than 10,000 'self-help' and community organisations in the United Kingdom, both national and local, are published by the Mental Health Foundation in their **Someone to Talk to Directory**, available through your local library. It might be worth your while to look at this. More general reading you might consider includes the excellent *Understanding Mental Health* by Angelina Gibbs, published by the Consumer's Association, and *First Aid in Mental Health* by Joy Melville, published as an Unwin Paperback. These books cover a wide variety of aspects of mental health, mostly from the viewpoint of the sufferer.

The National Schizophrenia Fellowship have published three books that give a very clear view of the problems of living with someone suffering from schizophrenia. These are *Schizophrenia at Home, Living with Schizophrenia — by the Relatives*, and the harrowing *A Tragedy of Schizophrenia: the Wife's Tale*. Finally, the Office of Health Economics has published a booklet entitled *Schizophrenia*.

Appendix
Useful Addresses

In this appendix we have listed organisations that may be of use to you or your relative, with a brief account of what they provide. Some are mentioned in more detail in the text, as indicated.

Association for Post-Natal Illness,
Institute of Obstetrics and Gynaecology,
Queen Charlotte's Maternity Hospital,
Goldhawk Road,
London W6 0X9.
(01) 748 4666

This organisation provides a countrywide network of volunteers available by phone, who have themselves recovered from post natal illness.

Association of Carers,
First Floor,
21–23 New Road,
Chatham,
Kent ME4 4QJ.
(0634) 813981

For a small membership fee this organisation will give you practical information about caring for your relative. They can put you in touch with carers in a similar situation. They are especially concerned to help carers avoid mental illness themselves.

Association of Community
  Health Councils for
  England and Wales,
Mark Lemon Suite,
254 Seven Sisters Road,
London N4 2HZ.
(01) 272 5459

These are organisations that
officially represent the
consumer's interest in the
National Health Service.
They are a useful source of
information about local
mental health facilities.
Local branches will be in
the phone book under
'community' or the name of
the District Health
Authority.

Association of Northern
  Ireland District
  Committees,
25–27 Adelaide Street,
Belfast BT2 8FH.
(0232) 224431

Association of Scottish
  Local Health Councils,
21 Torpichen Street,
Edinburgh EH3 8HX.
(031) 229 2344

British Association for
  Counselling,
37a Sheep Street,
Rugby,
Warwickshire CV21 3BX.
(0788) 78328

This association provides
information about available
counsellors and counselling
agencies.

British Medical Association,
BMA House,
Tavistock Square,
London WC1.
(01) 387 4499

The doctors' representative
organisation.

Brook Advisory Centre,
153a East Street,
London SE17 2SD.
(01) 708 1234/1390

Advice on emotional and
sexual problems,
contraception. Local
branches.

Caribbean House Group,
Caribbean House,
Bridport Place,
Shoreditch Park,
London N1 5DS.
(01) 729 0986

Social work action for West Indians.

Carr-Gomm Society
  Limited,
38 Gomm Road,
Bermondsey,
London SE16.
(01) 231 9284

Hostels for the lonely and single.

Catholic Marriage Advisory
  Council,
15 Lansdowne Road,
London W1I 3AJ.
(01) 727 0141

This offers marital counselling to people of any or no denomination.

Charities Aid Foundation,
48 Pembury Road,
Tonbridge,
Kent TN9 2JD.
(0732) 356323

Citizens' Rights Office,

Practical help and advice on welfare rights.
4th Floor,
1–5 Bath Street,
London EC1V 9PY.

Court of Protection,
Staffordshire House,
Store Street,
London WC1E 7BP.
(01) 636 6877

See p. 77.

Depressives Anonymous,
  Fellowship of,
36 Chestnut Avenue,
North Humberside,
HU17 9QU.
(0482) 860619

This has a number of local groups. It offers mutual self-help, complementary to professional services. Newsletter and penfriend scheme.

Depressives Associated,
PO Box 5,
Castletown,
Portland,
Dorset DT5 1BQ.

Mutual help. More of a pressure group than the above as they think few doctors understand depression. Local groups. Information leaflets.

Disablement Income Group,
Attlee House,
28 Commercial Street,
London E1 6LR.
(01) 790 2424

Advises on financial problems, benefits and allowances. Local branches.

Ex-Services Mental Welfare
  Society,
Broadway House,
The Broadway,
London SW19 1RL.
(01) 543 6333

May provide charitable funds for eligible mentally ill people in financial difficulty.

Family Service Units,
207 Old Marylebone Road,
London NW1 5QP.
(01) 402 5175
(see local phone directory)

Provide support and services for couples with young children. Casework.

Family Welfare Association,
501–505 Kingsland Road,
Dalston,
London E8 4AU.
(01) 254 6251

Voluntary social work to families. Publishes Charities Digest and guide to the Social Services.

General Medical Council,
44 Hallam Street,
London W1N 6AE.
(01) 580 7642

Monitors the medical
professions' standards of
service and behaviour.

Health Service
  Commissioner for
  England,
Church House,
Great Smith Street,
London SW1P 3BW.
(01) 212 7676

Health Service
  Commissioner for
  Scotland,
2nd Floor,
11 Melville Crescent,
Edinburgh EH3 7LU.
(031) 225 7465

Health Service
  Commissioner for Wales,
4th Floor, Pearl Assurance
  House,
Greyfriars Road,
Cardiff CF1 3AG.
(0222) 394621

The health 'Ombudsman'. If
you are dissatisfied with the
way a complaint has been
handled by the hospital
authorities, you can take it
to the Health Commissioner.
The Northern Irish
equivalent is the
Commissioner for
Complaints.

Holiday Care Service,
2 Old Bank Chambers,
Station Road,
Horley,
Surrey RH6 9HW.
(0293) 774535

Provides information for
people with special holiday
needs, including the
mentally ill.

Jewish Marriage Council,
23 Ravenshurst Avenue,
London NW4 4EL.
(01) 203 6311

Offers marital counselling to
people of any or no
denomination.

Jewish Welfare Board,
221 Golders Green Road,
London NW11.
(01) 458 3282

Hostels.

Leonard Cheshire
   Foundation,
26–29 Maunsel Street,
London SW1.
(01) 828 1822

Hostels and domiciliary
support for mentally
handicapped and psychiatric
patients.

Manic Depression
   Fellowship,
51 Sheen Road,
Richmond,
Surrey.
(01) 940 6235

Support group for relatives.
See p. 135.

Marriage Guidance Council.
(See local phone directory)

Trained volunteers offer
counselling and practical
advice. Booklists and books.
Those who can afford it may
be asked to contribute to
costs.

Mental After-care
   Association,
Eagle House,
110 Jermyn Street,
London SW1Y 6HB.
(01) 839 5953

Homes and hostels in south-
east England for those
recovering from mental
illness. Fees usually paid by
DHSS or Local Authority.
Residents may be offered

counselling and social
activities. Referrals from
statutory authorities.

Mental Health Act
  Commission.
Write to the address nearest
  the hospital:

Room 22, Hepburn House,
Marsham Street,
London SW1P 4HW.
(01) 211 8061/8858

Cressington House,
249 St Mary's Road,
Garston,
Liverpool L19 0NF.
(051) 427 2061

Spur A Block 5,
Government Buildings,
Chalfont Drive,
Western Boulevard,
Nottingham NG8 3RZ.
(0602) 292997

See p. 147.

Mental Health Commission
  for Northern Ireland,
Elizabeth House,
116–118 Holywood Road,
Belfast BT4 1NY.
(0232) 651157

Mental Health Foundation,
8 Hallam Street,
London W1N 6DH.
(01) 580 0145

Provides general
information. Various
booklets. Funds research in
mental health and
innovative projects to help
the mentally ill, especially
in the community.

Mental Health Review
  Tribunals.
Write to the address nearest
  the hospital:

Room 1516, Euston Tower,
286 Euston Road,
London NW1 3DN.
(01) 388 1188 (ext 787)

3rd Floor, Cressington
  House,
249 St Mary's Road,
Garston,
Liverpool L19 0NF.
(051) 494 0095

Spur A Block 5,
Government Buildings,
Chalfont Drive,
Western Boulevard,
Nottingham NG8 3RZ.
(0602) 294222

2nd Floor, New Crown
  Buildings,
Cathays Park,
Cardiff CF1 3NQ.
(0222) 823398/825111

See p. 144.

Mental Welfare
  Commission for
  Scotland,
22 Melville Street,
Edinburgh EH3 7NS.
(031) 225 7034

The Scottish equivalent of
the Mental Health
Commission. See p. 149.

MIND HQ,
22 Harley Street,
London W1N 2ED.
(01) 637 0741

See index.

National Association of
  Voluntary Hostels,
33 Long Acre,
London WC2E 9LA.
(01) 240 3222

Useful source of
information about
availability.

National Council for Civil
  Liberties,
21 Tabard Street,
London SE1 4LA.
(01) 403 3888.

National Marriage Guidance
  Council,
Herbert Gray College,
Little Church Street,
Rugby,
Warwickshire CV21 3AP.
(0788) 73241

National Schizophrenia
    Fellowship,
78 Victoria Road,
Surbiton,
Surrey KT6 4NS.
(01) 390 3651

(Relatives' Centre)
17 Cannon Street,
Birmingham B2 5EN.
(021) 643 7980

National Schizophrenia
    Fellowship (Northern
    Ireland),
47 Rosemary Street,
Belfast BT1 1QB.
(0232) 248006

National Schizophrenia
    Fellowship (Scotland),
40 Shandwick Place,
Edinburgh EH2 4RT.
(031) 226 2025

Self help organisation for
relatives
See pp. 134–5

National Women's Aid
    Federation,
374 Grays Inn Road,
London WC1.
(01) 837 9316

Accommodation and
support for battered wives.

Northern Ireland
    Association for Mental
    Health,
Beacon House,
84 University Street,
Belfast BT7 IHE.
(0232) 228474

Northern Ireland branch of
    MIND.

Northern Ireland Mental
  Health Review Tribunal,
Mental Health Branch,
Room 3C Dundonald
  House,
Stormont Estate,
Belfast BT4 3FF.
(0232) 650111

See pp. 144, 149.

Northern Schizophrenia
  Fellowship,
38 Collingwood Buildings,
Collingwood Street,
Newcastle-upon-Tyne,
Tyne & Wear NEI IJH.
(0632) 614343

Affiliated to National
Schizophrenia Fellowship
Hostels and sheltered
workshops.

Office of Care and
  Protection,
Royal Courts of Justice,
Chichester Street,
Belfast BT1 3JF.
(0232) 235111

Northern Irish equivalent to
the English Court of
Protection.
See p. 77.

Patients' Association,
Room 33, 18 Charing Cross
  Road,
London WC2H 0HR.
(01) 240 0671

Independent organisation.
Pressure group for patients.
Advice and information.

Psychiatric Rehabilitation
  Association,
21a Kingsland High Street,
London E8 2JS.
(01) 254 9753

Various facilities in NE
London to help mental
patients re-establish
themselves in the
community. Group homes,
'cluster flats', intensive care
accommodation, support.
Advice to relatives.

Remploy Ltd,
415 Edgware Road,
London NW2 6LR.
(01) 452 8020

Sheltered employment.
Candidates selected by
Disablement Resettlement
Officer.

Richmond Fellowship,
8 Addison Road,
London W14 8DL.
(01) 603 6373

Hostels, homes and
workshops for recovering
mental patients.

Royal College of
    Psychiatrists,
17 Belgrave Square,
London SW1X 8PG.
(01) 235 2351

Representative organisation
of psychiatrists in UK. Sets
training standards.

Samaritans,
17 Uxbridge Road,
Slough,
Berks SL1 1SN.
(0753) 32713
(See local phone directory)

Will offer advice, support
and befriending by phone
to the despairing, or those
worried by someone who
is.

Schizophrenia Association
    of Great Britain,
Bryn Hyfryd,
The Crescent,
Bangor,
Gwynedd LL57 2AG.
(0248) 354048

Advice and information by
phone or letter. Have a
primarily 'biological' view
of schizophrenia.

Scottish Association for
    Mental Health,
40 Shandwick Place,
Edinburgh EH2 4RT.
(031) 225 4446

Scottish 'MIND'.

Simon Community,
129 Malden Road,
London NW5.
(01) 485 6639

Helps ex-psychiatric
patients, among others, to
find accommodation.

Tranx,
25 Masons Avenue,
Wealdstone,
Middlesex HA3 5AH.
(01) 427 2065

The National Tranquilliser
Advice Centre. Telephone
or group support for helping
people to come off
tranquillisers.

The Volunteer Centre,
29 Lower King's Road,
Berkhamsted,
Herts HP4 2AB.
(044 27) 73311

Information about local
voluntary facilities.

Women's Royal Voluntary
    Service,
234 Stockwell Road,
London SW9 9SP.
(01) 733 3388
(See local phone directory)

Meals on wheels.

Index